Home Electrical Wiring

A Complete Guide to Home Electrical Wiring

Explained by a
Licensed Electrical Contractor

Current with 2011 and 2013 Electrical Codes

by David W. Rongey

ISBN 978-0-9890427-0-3

Home·Electrical·Wiring

Prefix

Copyright Notice

ISBN 978-0-9890427-0-3

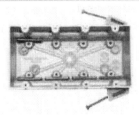

Home·Electrical·Wiring

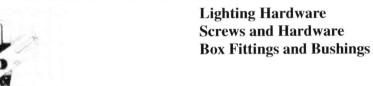

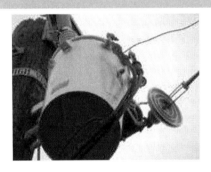

MAIN ELECTRICAL SERVICE PANELS
Overhead and Underground
Electrical Service
Overhead Electrical Services
Underground Electrical Services
Underground Service from a Pole
Mounted Transformer
Underground to a Pad Mounted
Transformer
Underground Conduit
Installation
Sub Panels
Junction Boxes and Pull Boxes
Circuit Breakers
Multi-wire Circuits
Aluminum Wire
Copper Wire
Panel Neutrals

GROUNDING and BONDING
Panel Grounds
Detached Building Grounds
Circuit Grounds
Grounding
Grounding and Bonding
Service Equipment Grounding
Ground Rod Installation
Foundation Ground Water &
Gas
Grounding Outlets
Grounding Switches
How to Ground a Breaker Panel

~Home·Electrical·Wiring~

AREAS and ROOMS

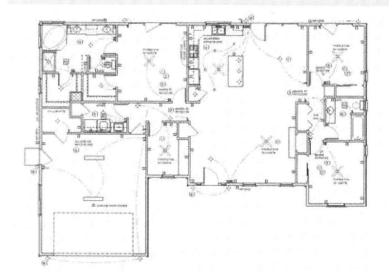

Main Plan - House
Kitchen
Kitchen and Dining Room
Dining Room
Master Bedroom
Master Bathroom
Bedrooms
Bathroom
Living Room and Entry
Laundry
Garage and Workshop
Basement

HOME ELECTRICAL CIRCUITS

Home Electrical Circuits
Electrical Circuit Schedule
Minimum Electrical Service Load
Calculator
Circuit Planner - Worksheet

120 VOLT CIRCUITS

20 Amp Circuit - Receptacles
20 Amp Circuit - GFCI
Receptacles
20 Amp Circuit - GFCI Breaker
20 Amp Circuit - GFCI:
Bathroom
20 Amp Circuit - GFCI: Kitchen
20 Amp Circuit -Garbage
Disposal - Switched Outlet

Home·Electrical·Wiring

240 VOLT CIRCUITS 301

EXTERIOR CIRCUITS 318

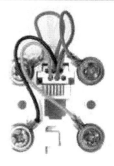

TROUBLESHOOTING 360

GLOSSARY 367

BONUS SECTION 376

INDEXES   383

RESOURCES   402

Preliminary

Book Preliminary

Home·Electrical·Wiring

Introduction and Disclaimer

Introduction:
WARNING: Some home improvement projects are dangerous by their very nature, and even the safest tool can cause serious injury or death if used incorrectly. Always read and follow instruction manuals and safety warnings. Always use common sense and take extra precautions when working with electricity.

Disclaimer Notice:
Ask-The-Electrician.com, Home-Electrical-Wiring, com and David W. Rongey do not accept any liability or responsibility for the information contained in this publication. You, the reader, assume full responsibility for your interpretation and actions as a result of any of this information. Any project of any kind that is performed based on information found in this book is therefore done at your own risk and is your responsibility, with you accepting the liability and responsibility for past, present, and future consequences of materials, structures and life associated with, and as a result of your work.

IF YOU ARE NOT COMFORTABLE WITH, OR DO NOT UNDERSTAND ANY OF THIS INFORMATION, OR YOU ARE UNSURE OF YOUR OWN ABILITY TO REASON, COMPREHEND, INTERPRET, OR PERFORM ANY WORK OF ANY TYPE BASED ON THE INFORMATION FOUND IN THIS BOOK, PLEASE DO NOT PARTICIPATE IN ANY MANNER OR PERFORM ANY ACTION, BUT CONSULT WITH A LICENSED, PROFESSIONAL ELECTRICAL CONTRACTOR WHO CAN DO THIS WORK FOR YOU.
YOU EXPRESSLY AGREE TO HOLD ASK-THE-ELECTRICIAN.COM, HOME-ELECTRICAL-WIRING.COM, DAVID W. RONGEY, AND THEIR EMPLOYEES, CONSULTANTS AND/OR EXPERTS AND ASSOCIATES HARMLESS FOR ANY PROPERTY DAMAGE, PERSONAL INJURY AND/OR DEATH, OR ANY OTHER LOSS OR DAMAGE THAT MAY RESULT FROM YOUR USE OF THE INFORMATION OR SERVICE PROVIDED HEREIN AND THROUGHOUT.

The NEC National Electrical Code is produced by the NFPA National Fire Prevention Association. The NEC electrical codes are published every three years and commonly adopted by state or local law. This publication may not include or reflect all code changes, modifications, amendments or updates. This publication is not a publication of the NFPA and has not been reviewed or authorized by the NFPA, and does not represent the NFPA, and should not be used in place of the NEC or NFPA publications.

By using this publication, including any content contained therein, the reader agrees that the use of this publication is entirely at his/her own risk and there is no warranty expressly made herein. If you do not agree with any of this statement or the statements found in the legal disclaimer, please stop reading this publication at once.

Even though codes are developed and enforced they may not be tested or evaluated for accuracy. The developers of codes and the author of this book disclaim any liability for personal injury, property damage of any nature whatsoever, directly or indirectly resulting from this publication, the use of or the reliance on this publication. The author makes no guarantee or warranty as to the accuracy or completeness of any information published herein.

Home·Electrical·Wiring

Overview: How this Book is Organized

My Goal for this Book
My goal for writing this book has been to produce the book I have never been able to find, which will provide quality information that is straight to the point with photos to help communicate the subject so the reader will have a good understanding of the material.

Organization of this Book
The book is organized the same way I approach any project, by identifying the basic fundamentals and knowledge needed to develop a successful project. Deeper into the book there is more detailed information for specific projects and circuits.

Sections
This book is divided into sections as described below. You may navigate to any section you wish where you will find a listing of the topics presented. You may also work your way through the book from start to finish and receive a well-rounded understanding of home electrical wiring.

Electrical Circuits and Electrical Codes
Within the book you will find CDTs' or Circuit Design Tables which will provide you with a good understanding of the typical components needed for installing circuits found in the home. You will also find extensive listings of organized, easy to understand electrical codes as they apply to specific a topic or project.

Please see the following page for the complete List of Sections.

About the Author

Hi! My name is Dave Rongey.

For over 38 years, I have enjoyed all aspects of electrical work...from custom homes to industrial automation.

I am also an avid "Do-It- Yourselfer"; and most of the time I'd rather not pay someone else to do something I know I can do myself. I have been working in the electrical industry since 1972 and have experience in residential, commercial and industrial areas of new construction, additions and remodels.

I have been recognized for saving thousands of dollars by implementing Energy Management and Building Automation projects for large facilities in leading fortune 500 companies. I have participated in several energy reduction projects with local electric utility companies where I helped customers reduce their electricity consumption.

My love for wiring Custom Homes in some of the most beautiful areas in California and for some of the nicest people on earth has produced a level of satisfaction my family and I now enjoy. Not long ago I decided to share my years of electrical experience on the internet so others can learn to perform do-it-yourself projects, improve the safety and comfort of their home, and have some fun in the process. As a Licensed Electrical Contractor, I have seen too many do-it-yourself projects performed by well-meaning people that are serious fire and safety hazards! I do not want you to take a chance on doing your next project wrong and becoming a headline in your hometown newspaper!

My desire is that Ask-The-Electrician.com and the books and project guides I am developing will be your source for the finest "Do It Yourself" electrical guidance... period! You will not find another resource of any kind, anywhere that provides more detailed instruction packed with over 38 years of hands-on experience. Let me work with you on your home electrical projects and increase the value of your beautiful home. With a track record of satisfied customers, I am helping people everywhere realize their dream of saving money and enhancing their home with beautiful electrical projects, increased safety, and security.

I 'm looking forward to assisting you with many projects!
Dave

Dedication

I would like to dedicate this book to my father, Thomas N. Rongey,
who taught me everything he knew about the electrical trade and business.
I worked on countless jobs with my Dad starting as a young boy holding a flashlight on late night emergency jobs where I was able to ask a lot of questions and learn first hand while he taught me how to do many aspects of electrical wiring and construction
- I miss you Dad!

I enjoyed having my son, Matthew, help me wire numerous custom homes, even during his summer breaks while at college - that was a lot of fun, and I'm so glad you were there with me. Matthew took a lot of on-the-job photos and videos, some of which are in this book and more will be featured in future publications.
Matthew also did a great job writing two books about Outdoor Lighting and Solar Lighting.
Thanks Buddy!

My wife Carol and daughter Sarah are my all important home support team where they help out with various tasks that help me with my business, but most of all we are all a working family that still has time for some fun after the late nights and long projects are completed.

Home Improvement

HOME IMPROVEMENT

Home Improvement Projects

Home Wiring Projects, Codes and this Publication

The advice and information found at Ask-The-Electrician.com, Home-Electrical-Wiring.com, and in this publication may not reflect what is experienced at your home project location. Although we make every effort to duplicate several known project scenarios we may not represent your exact situation. Ask-The-Electrician.com, Home-Electrical-Wiring.com, David W. Rongey and their associates are not responsible for the existing wiring methods and practices that are found in your home.

Only upon proper qualified training from an approved source will you be qualified to inspect and make a full assessment of the electrical systems at your home. Ask-The-Electrician.com, Home-Electrical-Wiring.com and Dave Rongey provide information focusing on particular aspects of projects, which will be represented to the best of our ability, but may not represent your exact project or your scope of work. If at any time you are unsure about how to work with or complete any component or aspect of your electrical project, you are advised to hire a licensed electrical contractor to do the work for you.

Please refer to the Disclaimer Notice in this publication for more information.

Home Electrical Wiring

Planning the Project

Steps to Successful Home Electrical Wiring

✔ Plan the installation of your electrical project or device.

✔ Produce a set of blueprint drawings or plans.

✔ Investigate local electrical codes compliance and ordinances.

✔ Submit the set of plans for approval and obtain an electrical permit.

✔ Determine the required electrical circuit power.

✔ Determine the electrical wire size and circuit protection.

✔ If branching from an existing electrical circuit, then match the existing wire gauge and insulation type.

✔ Identify the electrical wiring path and components necessary to protect the circuit wiring.

✔ Develop a material list, call for competitive electrical materials pricing, and purchase materials.

✔ Locate or contract special electrical tools, equipment or services.

✔ Install the circuit components at the appropriate phase of construction project.

✔ Attach ground bonding, identify and make up wiring splices.

✔ Verify the circuit path and components, and then test the electrical circuit.

✔ Schedule and obtain electrical inspections for each phase of the project.

Electrical Symbols

Ø	110 OUTLET COUNTER
	110 DUPLEX OUTLET, +15 U.O.N.
	220 OUTLET, DRYER RECEPTACLE
	GFI OUTLET (DEVICE W/ GFCI PROTECTION) EXTERIOR OUTLET SHALL HAVE WATERPROOF COVER
AFCI	ARC-FAULT CIRCUIT INTERRUPTER
	DUPLEX 110 HALF HOT HALF ACTIVATED BY SWITCH
$	SINGLE POLE SWITCH, +48"
$³	3-WAY SWITCH, +48"
$⁴	4-WAY SWITCH, +48"
	WALL MOUNTED LIGHT FIXTURE (EXTERIOR)
	LIGHT FIXTURE- WALL MOUNT, 6'-8"
	CEILING LIGHT FIXTURE- CEILING MOUNTED
	RECESSED LIGHT FIXTURE
J	FAN J BOX
	UNDER CABINET FLUORESCENT LIGHT
	LIGHTED ADDRESS NO, +52"
	WALL SCONCE
	200 AMP ELECTRICAL SERVICE PANEL
(E) (G)	HOUSE PANEL (E) ELECTRICAL (G) GAS METER
F J	FUSED DISCONNECT, VERIFY WIRING REQUIREMENTS WITH UNIT NAME PLATE

S	EXHAUST FAN
	COMBO. LIGHT/FAN
F	RECESSED FLUORESCENT
SD	SINGLE STATION SMOKE DETECTOR, 110V W/ BATTERY BACKUP, INTERCONNECTED, CEILING MOUNTED
A	LOW-VOLT BACKLIT ADDRESS MARKER
	SPECIAL PURPOSE OUTLET/DISCONNECT
*	DOORBELL, PUSH BUTTON STATION, +48", WP
	DOORBELL CHIME, +6'-8"
T	THERMOSTAT
TV	CABLE OUTLET, +15"
	SINGLE TELEPHONE/DATA OUTLET, +15", U.O.N.
	2-TUBE FLUORESCENT LIGHT
	4-TUBE FLUORESCENT
	CAT5/RG6 NETWORK PANEL
	DATA
T	CLOCK TIMER

OHM's Law

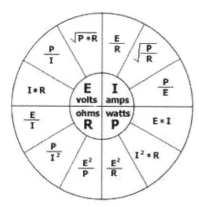

OHM's Law Formula and how it is used for determining electrical loads as it pertains to watts, volts and amps. OHM's Law is very helpful to help us understand sizing electrical circuits for the home electrical system.

Basic OHM'S Law		
I	Current	Measured in Amps
P	Power	Measured in Watts
R	Resistance	Measured in OHMs
E	Voltage	Measured in Volts

OHM's Law Formulas		
AMPS	=	Watts / Volts
	OR	
I	=	P / E
WATTS	=	Amps x Volts
	OR	
P	=	I x E

OHM's Law Examples		
AMPS	=	Watts / Volts
16.6	=	4000 / 240
WATTS	=	Amps x Volts
4000	=	16.6 x 240

Safety

SAFETY

Electrical Safety

Do Not Work on Live Panels or Energized Wiring!

⚠ **DANGER**

HAZARD OF
ELECTRICAL
SHOCK, CONTACT
WILL CAUSE
SEVERE INJURY
OR DEATH.

TURN OFF AND
LOCK OUT POWER
TO THIS DEVICE
BEFORE
SERVICING.

Electrical Safety Checklist
Before working with electrical wiring:

#1. Test the Circuit
Always use a good quality tester.

#2. Positively Identify the Circuit
Identify and label the circuit(s).

#3. Turn the Circuit Off
Shut the circuit off before beginning any work.

#4. Post a Note at the Panel or Power Source
Advise others that you are working on the circuit wiring.

The Same Thing that Killed this Poor Little Mouse can Kill Anyone.

I have seen this more than once and it always sends a message that is Loud and Clear to me!
Electricity is one of those two edge swords, it can be used for good, or it can kill you, just like this poor little mouse. It's a sad story, but this poor little mouse found a nice warm place on top of this 200 amp Main Circuit Breaker in a house electrical panel, but the mouse did not understand the danger involved. At last the poor little mouse snuggled in just a little too close and **got fried!**

OK, So What's the Message for us Here?
In the midst of getting a little too comfortable or over confident with our work it is easy to become vulnerable of the wrong side of electricity.
Be Careful, Be Smart and Don't take Chances
Far worse than costing you a lot of money is the value of human life. Yes, electricity can kill, just as it did the poor little mouse, so be careful and think it through.

Home·Electrical·Wiring

Personal Safety and Protection

 **A Hard Hat may be required on some job sites.**

Safety Glasses

 Dust Mask

 Ear Protection

 **Work Gloves and Knee Pads**

Work Boots and Protective Clothing

Ladder Safety

Be well supported and braced when using power tools while on a ladder.

Use only well supported Non-Conductive Ladders with proper weight ratings.

Roof Safety

When working on the roof; make sure that you, your tools, and materials are safely secured with a rope.

Safety on the Job Pg-1

Be Careful, Be Safe, and Don't Get Hurt!
Things to Look Out For

For smaller projects a few GFCI Protected circuits may be all that is required to keep the power tools working.

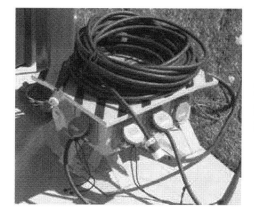

For big jobs, this is my favorite temporary power unit which provides multiple circuits of GFCI Protected power for several receptacles to help keep the job going and on schedule.

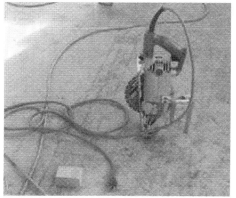

Be aware of potential dangerous conditions due to the working habits of other contractors. If you see something that is unsafe, bring it to the attention of the job foreman or general contactor.

Be Careful, Be Safe, and Don't Get Hurt!
Things to Look Out For

Essential building materials and tools may be all over the place if the project is being rushed along. In a case like this I will look for an area to work that isn't over occupied or I will just return when there aren't so many things happening all at once. Making good use of my time helps me to stay focused and get more work done.

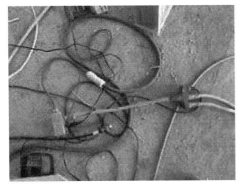

When a lot of work is being done by several trades' people there will be a web of extension cords everywhere which can cause a tripping hazard so watch your step!

A scaffold with safety rails and locking wheels is very helpful when working in high ceilings. The scaffold may be shared by several contractors so be aware when it is in use and stay clear directly below.

Safety in the Attic Pg-1

Depending on the location, the attic can get extremely hot during summer months and should be avoided during the hottest times of the day.

Take all necessary safety precautions
and protect yourself against the conditions and elements in the attic area. Suggestions: Overalls, Stocking Cap, Flash Light or Drop Light and GFCI Protection.
If the insulation is deep then a section of cardboard might be helpful.

Roof trusses in the attic are like an obstacle course. Make sure to have a good source of light and be careful not to bang your head, especially if you're wearing a hat that blocks your upper view.

Deep amounts of blown in insulation create a challenge when locating electrical wiring.

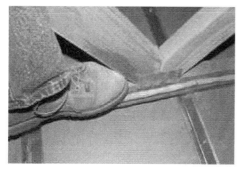

In non-insulated attic spaces it is much easier to see where I can walk and it's much easier to locate cables if needed.

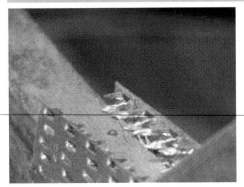

Most roofing truss supports are held in place by these metal nail plates which can be extremely sharp on the open points and the edges as well. Be very careful and do NOT run wire on top of these or the cable sheath may get damaged.

Deep insulation makes it very easy to lose tools but a bright light will help you keep track and get the job done.

Make sure your power source is GFCI - Ground Fault Protected.

Hornets and wasps are sometimes found on the jobsite during the hot summer months. A shot of wasp spray in the morning will help out if they become a problem.

In older homes there may be vermiculite insulation which should be avoided or removed by an approved contractor because of possible health hazards. Make sure to wear a mask for protection.

Home·Electrical·Wiring

Safety Under the House

Never work on energized circuits while under a house, remember that you are in direct contact with the earth ground.

<u>Take all necessary Safety Precautions</u>
and protect yourself against the conditions and elements under the home.
Suggestions:
Overalls, Stocking Cap, Flash Light or Drop Light and GFCI Protection.
If the soil area is really rocky then a section of cardboard will be more comfortable to lie on.

Some crawl spaces are tight and flooring supports and beams can produce a nasty bump on the head, so be careful!

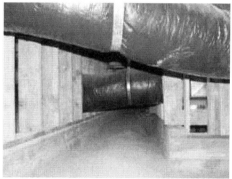

Heating and air conditioning ducts are a common obstacle causing you to either climb over or crawl under to get where you need to work, so be careful not to damage these.

Poisonous spiders, snakes and other critters might be in your area so be careful. Usually they don't come looking for you but you should be on the look out.

Electrical Tools

TOOLS

Electricians' Pouch of Hand Tools

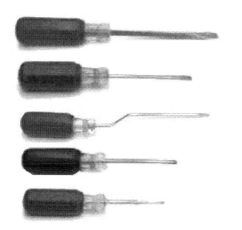

Large Screw Driver

Medium Screw Driver

Offset Screw Driver

Phillips Screw Driver

Awl

Lineman's Pliers

Crimp Pliers

Needle Nose Pliers

Wire Strippers

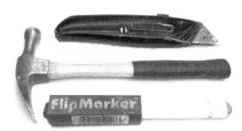

Utility Knife or Sheath Stripper

Long Nose Hammer

Pencil and Keel/Crayon

Tools for Rough-In Wiring

Rough-In Wiring Tool Tray

Drill Bits
Chuck Keys
Allen Wrenches
Cable Staples

Heavy Duty Drill Motor
with Half Inch Chuck

Drill Bits:
Installer Bit
Ship Auger Bits
Self Feeding Bit
Hole Saw
Chuck Key

25 Foot Tape Measure

Measure Twice,
Install Once!

Permanent Marker

Marking the location of
junction boxes and fixtures

Magnetic Speed Level

Level and Accuracy

Plumb Bob

Handy for locating light
fixtures with a floor layout.

Battery Operated Tools

Drill Motor
Half Inch Chuck, Variable Speed, and Torque Settings.

Reciprocating Saw

Flash Light
Hand held or place in position

Head Mounted Flash Light
Hands free, shines where you're looking.

Stud Finder
Locate framing and other obstacles inside the wall.

Laser Plumb Bob
Handy for locating light fixtures from a floor layout.

Data Com Tools and Accessories

Punch Down Tool	Punch phone wires into the connector block
Cable Scissors	Cut and strip data-com cables.
RG6 Cable Stripper	Removes the outer jacket and exposes the inner core.
F-Connector Tool	Compresses the F-connector to the RG6 cable.
RJ Crimp Tool	Compresses the F-connector to the RG6 cable.
T25 Stapler	Secures data-com cables.

Data Com Accessories

Tie-Wraps / Zip Ties	Secures data-com cable bundles.
Scotch 3M UL Splice, with corrosion inhibitor	Splice for telephone cables. Insert wires and compress the connector.
RJ11 or RJ 45 Connector	Connector body for telephone and data
RG6 Connector, Coupling and Splitter	CCTV and cable modem service

Specialty Tools

**Hydraulic KO
Knock-Out Punches**

Create openings into panels and enclosures.

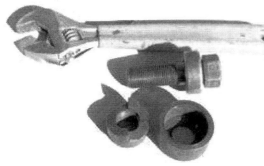

KO - Knock-Out Punches

Create openings into panels, enclosures and boxes.

The Fish Steel is used for pulling wires into conduits.

A fish steel should not be used for fishing wires through walls because it will wind up and get caught inside walls, and being metal it can be a shock hazard. Fishing through walls should be done using a fiberglass rod.

Cats Paw

Pulling nails out of framing.

Key Hole Saw

Cut openings into sheet rock.

Chain Pliers

Adjusting the chain for light fixtures.

Testers and Meters

Inductive Voltage Tester

For testing voltage of wiring and devices 120 to 600 Volts AC DC.
I use this type of tester the most, because it produces a quick accurate reading where I can feel the induction coil and see the neon light display.

Multi-Function Digital Meter, Clamp-On Amp Reading
Voltage and Continuity

This is a great all-in-one meter used for clamp-on amperage readings or a set of test leads for checking voltage or OHM's and continuity.

Non-Contact Voltage Tester. The non-conductive probe senses voltage.

Non-conductive testers are very handy but are not totally accurate because some may produce false readings so they should not be 100% relied on.

Plug-In Circuit Analyzer

3-Light Display detects the wiring configuration.
Plug in circuit analyzers are great but they too are not totally accurate and may produce false readings for boot-legged grounds and neutrals and even reverse polarity.

Analog Tester
Non-Conductive probe senses Voltage

The good old sweep-needle analog tester has been my buddy for a long time for testing voltage and OHMs or continuity for AC and DC circuits.

 **Home·Electrical·Wiring**

Materials

ELECTRICAL MATERIALS

Main Material Sections

Wire and Cable
Boxes and Enclosurers
Gutters and Pull Boxes
Conduits and Fittings
Wiring Devices
Lighting Controls

Wire and Cable

Home·Electrical·Wiring

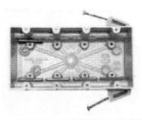

BOXES and ENCLOSURES

Home·Electrical·Wiring

GUTTERS and PULL BOXES

WIRING DEVICES

Home·Electrical·Wiring

LIGHTING CONTROLS

Wire Conductors

The most common type of home electrical wire that is installed for general purpose electrical circuits is known as Type NM or Non-Metallic sheathed cable, made up of at least one pair of insulated wire conductors and one bare wire used for the ground conductor. The ground conductor is bonded throughout the home to maintain a contiguous grounded system which originates back at the Main Service Panel.

The installation of the Type NM Cable home electrical wire is accomplished by drilling holes using approved methods which protects the wire and maintains structural integrity for the home. Methods are available to protect wiring which becomes vulnerable to damage which could occur during the installation of sheet rock or other wall coverings. This protection is provided by installing Safety Plates where required.

Wire Ampacity

The insulated Romex wiring conductors are rated for temperature.

This rating limits the current flow in amperage thereby preventing the wire from overheating and causing a fire.

Using the properly sized wire will ensure safe circuit performance.

Circuit Cables Pg-1

Interior Cables

Type NM Wire	Name & Amps	Typical Use
	14-2 Romex 15 Amps	Receptacles and Lighting
	14-3 Romex 15 Amps	Lighting - 3-Way Switches and Smoke Detectors
	12-2 Romex 20 Amps	Receptacles
	12-3 Romex 20 Amps	3-Wire Circuits - Kitchen / Garage
	10-2 Romex 30 Amps	Water Heaters - Small A/C
	10-3 Romex 30 Amps	Dryers 4-Wire Receptacle
	8-3 Romex 40 Amps	Small Ovens

Circuit Cables Pg-2

Armored Cable

Type BX Cable	Name & Amps	Typical Use
	#12-3 Conductors - 20 Amps	Receptacles and Lighting

---

Exterior Underground Feeder Cables

Cable Type	Name & Amps	Typical Use
	12-2 Type UF - 20 Amps 12-3 Type UF - 20 Amps	Receptacles and Lighting

---

Interior Single Conductors

Conductor	Description	Applications
	Copper Wire Solid or Stranded: #14 to #6 THHN or THWN	Receptacles Lighting Appliances Equipment

---

Service Conductors

Service Entrance Cables

**3-Wire with Ground
Type SE - Aluminum**

240 Volt Service Feeder

**3-Wire with Ground
Type SE - Aluminum**

240 Volt Large Equipment

Service Conductors

**Copper Conductors
1/0 to 4/0**

240 Volt Main Feeder

**Aluminum Conductors
1/0 to 4/0**

240 Volt Main Feeder

Main Service Conductors

**Copper Conductors
250 to 750 MCM**

240 Volt Main Feeder

**Aluminum Conductors
250 to 750 MCM**

240 Volt Main Feeder

Exterior Feeder Cables

Overhead Triplex

**Utility Service Drop
to the Main Panel**

**Direct Burial Triplex
Type USE**

240 Volt Feeder

NOTE: Determine the type and size of conductors using the Ampacity Table (Pg. 76) and local codes.

Cable Fasteners and Protection

STAPLING NM CABLE

Fastener	Description	Application
	Romex Staple Fasten cables to wood structure every 4-1/2' and within 8 " of boxes.	7/16 - #14 Romex
	Romex Staple Fasten cables to wood structure every 4-1/2' and within 8 " of boxes.	9/16 - #12 & #10 Romex
	Romex Staple Fasten cables to wood structure every 4-1/2' and within 8 " of boxes.	1 - Inch for Larger Cables

STAPLING LARGER CABLE

 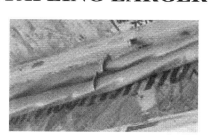

SE Cable
Round or smooth drive strap

CABLE PROTECTION

Safety Nail Plate

Protect the wires in vulnerable areas

Wire Connectors and Splicing Pg-1

Wire Connectors

WIRE CONNECTOR	DESCRIPTION	CAPACITY
	Large Blue Wire Connector	#14 thru #6 AWG Min. 3 #12 Max. 2 #6 w/ 1 #12
	Large Gray Wire Connector	#18 to #6 AWG Min. 2 #12 Max. 6 #12
	Red Wire Connector	#18 thru #8 AWG Min. 2 #18 Max. 4 #10
	Yellow Wire Connector	#18 thru #10 AWG Min. 2 #18 Max. 3 #12
	Orange Wire Connector	#22 to #14 AWG Min. 1 #18 w/ 1 #20 Max. 4 #16 w/ 1 #20

Moisture Resistant Wire Connectors

	Corrosive Resistant	#14 thru #10 AWG

	Butt, Fork, Spade, Ring	#14 thru #10 Stranded Wire

Home·Electrical·Wiring

Wire Connectors and Splicing Pg-2

Non Insulated Splice Connectors

Kearney-Split Bolt   **Various Sizes**

Lug Terminal   **Various Sizes**

Splice Connection Accessories

Anti-Corrosion Inhibitor   **Aluminum Wire Connections Lugs, Terminals, Splices**

Insulated Pad   Used with larger conductor splices. Fold the pad over the Kearney splice.

Electrical Tape   **Wrap layers of tape over finished splice**

Electrical Coating   Coating for outdoor electrical splices. Apply to the outside of the finished splice.

Wire Connectors and Splicing Pg-3

Insulated Splice Connectors

Kearney-Split Bolt   **Various Sizes**

Kearney-Split Bolt   **Various Sizes**

Direct Burial Splice Connectors

**Inline Direct Burial
Submersible Splice
Hex Screw Terminal**   **Various Sizes**

**Heat Shrink Tubing and Butt
Splice Screw Terminal**   **Various Sizes**

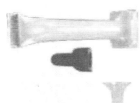
Waterproof Splice   **#14 - #10
Various Sizes**

**Inline Splice
Epoxy Mold**   **Various Sizes**

Boxes for New and Remodel Projects Pg-1

Receptacle Outlet and Switch Boxes

Electrical boxes shown are the plastic and fiberglass types typically used with NM-Type cable.

NOTE: Electrical boxes have wire size and quantity limitations, the boxes typically have the wire limitations indicated, also see the Box-Fill Table.

Electrical Box	Trade Name	Application
	**1-Gang Plastic Nail Box used with Romex cable wiring.** **Also known as a Rough-In Box.**	**Outlets and Switches.**

Multi-Gang Boxes

	2 and 3-Gang Boxes. Side Nail and Face Nail.	**Outlets and Switches. Face Nail is great for tight areas with limited room to nail.**
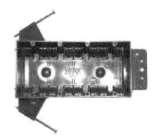	**4-Gang Plastic Nail Box.**	**Switches and lighting controls. Side Nail with face nailed opposite side due to length.**
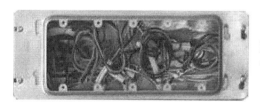	**Metal Multi-Gang Box with Trim Ring**	**Switches and lighting controls.**

Boxes for New and Remodel Projects Pg-2

Light Fixture Boxes

Electrical boxes shown are the plastic and fiberglass type typically used with NM-Type cable.

Electrical Box	Trade Name	Application
	3 and 4 -Inch Fiberglass Nail Box	Lighting fixtures and junctions.
	3 or 4 Inch Box with a Spanner Bracket. Spanner brackets also available for Metal Pancake Boxes.	Lighting Fixtures Mounted on the surface of the framing to be flush with finished sheet rock.
	3-Inch Metal Pancake Box. Also available in Fiberglass.	Lighting Fixtures Mounted on the surface of the framing to be flush with finished sheet rock.
	4-Inch Ceiling Fan Box	Ceiling Fan Pancake Box Approved for 70 lb. support.

Cut-In Boxes for New and Remodel Construction

Single Cut-In Boxes

Electrical boxes shown are the plastic and fiberglass type typically used with NM-Type cable.

Electrical Box	Trade Name	Application
 	1-Gang Metal and Fiberglass Cut-In Boxes	Outlets and Switches Used with Type-NM wiring in new or remodel applications.

Multi-Gang Cut-In Boxes

	2 and 3-Gang Fiberglass Cut-In Box	Outlets and Switches

Fixture Cut-In Boxes

	3-Inch Fiberglass Cut-In or Remodel Box	Lighting Fixtures and Smoke Detectors
	The 3" and 4" Metal Pancake Boxes Also available in Fiberglass.	Lighting Fixtures Pancake boxes are not the Cut-In type, but can be used when internal framing prevents using a cut-in fixture box where the pancake box may be mounted directly to the face of a stud.

Special Boxes and Accessories

Box Types for Special Applications

Electrical Box	Feature	Application
	Depth of Boxes	Box depth selection may vary for mounting restrictions or for wire Box Fill (Pg 81) requirements.
	Box Mounting Types	Box Mount Types include: Side Nailed Face Mounted Cut-In

Box Extensions

Box extensions may be needed when the face of the box is set back and not flush with the finished wall.

	2-Gang Fiberglass Cut-In Box	Outlets and Switches
	3-Gang Plastic Side Nail Box	Outlets and Switches

Ceiling Fan Boxes

Ceiling Fan Rated Boxes

4-Inch Ceiling Fan Flat Pancake Box

Ceiling Fan Pancake Box Approved for 70 lb. support.

4-Inch Ceiling Fan Stud Mounted Box

Plastic Ceiling Fan Box Approved for 70 lb. support.

4-Inch Ceiling Fan Bracket Box

Ceiling Fan Pancake Box Approved for 70 lb. support.

4-Inch Ceiling Fan Bracket Box

Ceiling Fan Box Ceiling Joist Adjustable Good for remodel insertion.

Outdoor Weather Proof Boxes

Weather Proof Switch and Receptacle Boxes

1-Gang Plastic Nail Box used for
Romex wiring
Also known as a Rough-In Box.

Outlets and Switches

1-Gang Fiberglass Cut-In Box with a
Back Bracket

Outlets and Switches
Romex wiring
Used with Romex wiring in remodel
applications.

Weather Proof Covers Boxes

2-Gang Plastic Nail Box

Outlets and Switches

Weather Proof Light Fixture Boxes

1-Gang Metal Cut-In Box
with Adjusting Mounting Ears

Outlets and Switches
With knock-outs for steel or aluminum
flex

Weather Proof Fixture Applications

2-Gang Plastic Face Nail Box

Outlets and Switches
Great for tight areas with limited room
to nail.

3-Gang Plastic Side Nail Box.

Outlets and Switches.

4-Square Metal Boxes

4"Square Boxes, also available in 5" Square (4-11/16")

Metal boxes can be used with conduit, flex or jacketed or sheathed cables, available in various depths, with or without side mounting brackets.
Approved connectors must be used for each application.

Electrical Box	Trade Name	Application
	4-Square Metal Box Use with raised rings for 1 or 2 Gangs, 3-0 or 4-0 openings.	**Receptacles and Switches** Surface mount for use in garage or shop area with EMT or Flex Conduit.
	4-SQ. Box Extension Use to increase the capacity of an existing 4-Sq. box.	Typically used in junction box applications with a blank 4-sq. cover.
	4-Sq. Raised Ring/Mud Ring Typically used with sheet rocked walls.	**Receptacles and Switches** Surface mount for use in garage or shop area with EMT or Flex Conduit.
	4-Sq. Flat Ring.	Shop area where a device cover plate will be installed.
	4-Sq. Blank Cover	Used as the cover for 4-Square boxes to protect electrical wiring and spliced wires.
	4-Sq. Raised Receptacle Cover	4-Sq. Raised Covers are available for receptacles and switches. Applications such as workshop or garage areas with EMT or Flex Conduit.

NOTE: All metal boxes require a blank cover or a cover which is used with a device.

Metal Boxes

3" and 4" Octagon Boxes

Electrical Box	Trade Name	Application
	4-Square Metal Box Use with raised rings for 1 or 2 Gangs, 3-0 or 4-0 openings.	**Receptacles and Switches** Surface mount for use in garage or shop area with EMT or Flex Conduit.

Single or Multi-Gang Metal Boxes

	1-Gang Handy Box Handy Extension boxes are also available.	**Outlets and Switches** Surface mount microwave receptacle. Garage or shop area with Conduit.

APPLICATION NOTE:

Single or multi-devices, available in various depths, with or without side mounting brackets, also available for masonry or concrete applications.

Metal boxes can be used with conduit, flex or jacketed or sheathed cables, available in various depths, with or without side mounting brackets. Approved connectors must be used for each application.

Conduits and Fittings

EMT
Electrical Metallic Tubing
Thin Wall

Thin wall
Above-ground Work

Set Screw Connector and Coupling. Compression and Insulated Connector. 1 or 2 Hole Strap (Set-Screw or Rain Tight)

Rigid Electrical Pipe
Thick Wall

Thick wall
Above or Underground Work

Threaded Coupling
Threadless Connector
Threadless Coupling
2 Hole Strap

PVC
Poly Vinyl Chloride
Schedule 40 and 80
also Flex Type

Thickness per application
Above or Underground Work

Straight Connector
Coupling
1 or 2 Hole Strap

Flex Conduits and Fittings

Steel or Aluminum Flex   **Above-Ground Work**

Straight Connector
90 Degree Con.
Coupling
EMT Conduit Adapter
1 or 2 Hole Strap

Seal Tight Flex with Reinforced
Steel flex inside and a PVC jacket   **Above or Underground Work**
on the outside

Straight Connector
45 degree connector
90 degree connector
2 Hole Strap

Flexible PVC   **Above or Underground Work,**
Just like PVC conduit but flexible   **great for deck lighting and**
outlets.

Straight PVC or Compression
connector.

1 or 2 Hole Strap

IMC "Smurf" Tubing, also   **Above ground, inside walls or**
available in orange for low voltage   **attics where approved.**
applications.   **Installs fast, easy to cut,**
compatible with PVC fittings.

Straight PVC Connector.

1 or 2 Hole Strap

Conduit Bodies

Conduit bodies are great for installing conduit with little or no bending, and they are very helpful for getting around tight corners. Install a connector into each opening for the type of conduit being installed.

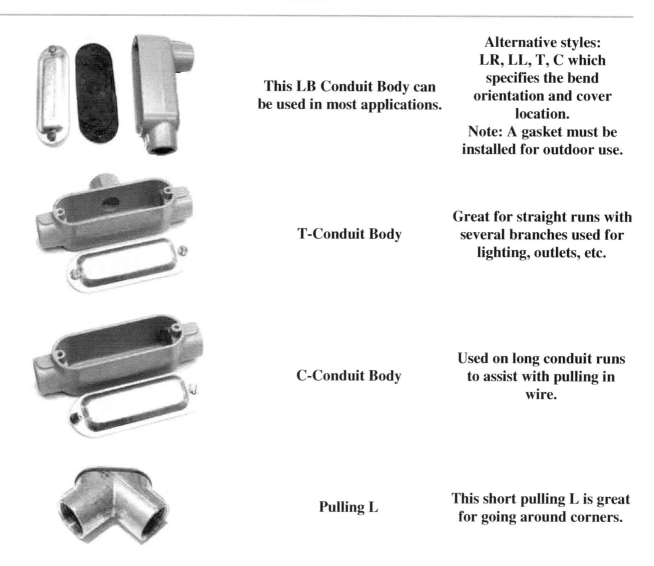

This LB Conduit Body can be used in most applications.

Alternative styles: LR, LL, T, C which specifies the bend orientation and cover location.
Note: A gasket must be installed for outdoor use.

T-Conduit Body

Great for straight runs with several branches used for lighting, outlets, etc.

C-Conduit Body

Used on long conduit runs to assist with pulling in wire.

Pulling L

This short pulling L is great for going around corners.

Note:
Wire splices may be made inside of conduit bodies if there is enough capacity for the number and size of wires.
Because conduit bodies have covers they must be accessible.

Conduit Benders and Bending

Types of Conduit Benders

Full Size 90 Degree　　　**Short Radius**　　　**Offset Bender**　　　**Rigid Pipe Hickey**

Bending conduit is best accomplished on a level surface.

Bending is best done on a level surface where steady pressure may be applied as the bend is made.

Additional bends may be needed for an offset bend or a saddle bend.

After the bends are complete and final cuts are made, make sure to ream the inside of the conduit to clean up any metal burrs and sharp edges that can damage wire insulation.

Home·Electrical·Wiring

Large Boxes: Gutters, Pull and Splice

Junction Boxes and Pull Boxes

Electrical Box	Feature	Application
	Gutter type Junction Box rated for indoor use	Wire splicing and conduit intersection.

This gutter type Pull Can or Junction Box is very handy when there are several conduits that will be entering into one location.

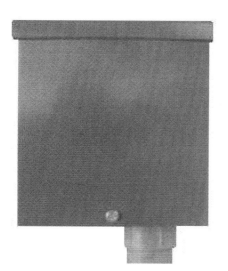	Metal Junction Box or Pull Can rated for outdoor use	Wire splicing and conduit intersection.

This Pull Can or Junction Box may be used to splice several wires or it may be used for mounting control devices such as relays or contactors.

Enclosure Box Applications

Applications for Junction Boxes and Pull Boxes

This metal Rain Tight box is being used as an enclosure for relay contactors as part of an ice melting system.

This PVC Rain Tight enclosure is being used a junction box to splice circuits for an electrical service panel upgrade project.

Receptacles - 120 Volt

Receptacle	Description	Application Example
	Duplex Receptacle 120 Volt 15 Amp	General purpose receptacle, such as the living room etc.
	Single Receptacle 120 Volt 15 Amp	Specific applications where an additional outlet is not wanted.
	Duplex Receptacle 120 Volt 20 Amp	For 20 AMP circuits only. Kitchen, Garage etc.
	Single Receptacle 120 Volt 20 Amp	May be installed on a dedicated circuit with a specific application such as vacuum system where a GFCI is not needed.
	GFCI Ground Fault Circuit Interrupter Receptacle 120 Volt 15 Amp	Kitchen Bathroom Garage Outdoor

Note: Tamper proof receptacles may be required, check with your local building department.

240 Volt Receptacles and Circuits

Typically these 240 volt appliances have a cord and require a receptacle outlet.

	240 Volt 30 Amp	**Electric Clothes Dryer**

	240 Volt 50 Amp	**Electric Range**

Typically these 240 Volt Circuits are hardwired and do not have a receptacle outlet.

	240 Volt **Amperage determined by unit and features**	**Oven** **or Oven Combination**

	240 Volt **Amperage determined by unit and features**	**Electric Stove** **or Cook Top**

	240 Volt 30 Amp	**Electric Water Heater**

	240 Volt **Amperage determined by the specific unit size**	**Air Conditioner**

Arc Fault Circuit Interrupter – AFCI

Electric circuit protection with AFCI provides the extra measure of safety for your family. AFCI's are installed serving required house wiring circuits, protecting areas such as the bedrooms. AFCI protects the bedroom circuit devices against the danger of arcing which can lead to fire.

The electric circuit breakers serving your home wiring circuits are intended for switching and protection of your home's wiring from high temperatures caused by excess current higher than the rating of the wire. While thermal magnetic circuit breakers are the key element for overload and short circuit protection of your home electrical system, there are potentially dangerous conditions that do not involve overcurrent. The following circuit breakers should be utilized to provide further protection with house wiring.

Combination
Arc Fault Circuit Interrupters (AFCI)

Combination AFCI's protect against all three possible types of arc fault: line to ground, line to neutral arcs, and series arcs and thus significantly reduce the risk of electrical fires. They feature a unique LED trip indicator, providing a valuable analysis tool to help pinpoint the type of trip and reduce the time spent debugging the home electrical wiring circuits.

Branch/Feeder
Arc Fault Circuit Interrupters (AFCI)

AFCI's are new electrical safety devices used for some of the home electrical wiring circuits that provide protection against arcing faults. These devices recognize characteristics unique to arcing and de-energize the circuit when an arc fault is detected. Arc faults may occur for many reasons such as worn electrical insulation or damaged wire, misapplied or damaged appliance cords and equipment, loose electrical connections, or driving a nail into a wall and having it inadvertently hit a wire. The possibility of arcing grows as a home ages since age and time will contribute to the possibility of these conditions occurring.

GFCI Receptacle

Wiring for Different Types of GFCI Protection

A GFCI Receptacle Outlet has LINE and LOAD terminals for both the hot and neutral wires. The wiring configuration for the LINE and LOAD will determine the type of GFCI protection. The face or front of the GFCI Outlet has TEST and RESET buttons for easy operation.

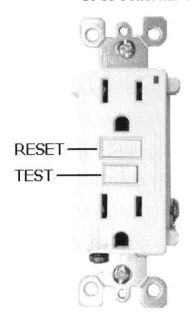

RESET—

TEST—

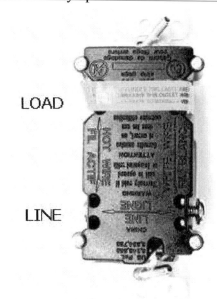

LOAD

LINE

GFCI Protection with LINE and LOAD Wiring Configurations

LINE

2-wire romex with ground

Power in from panel

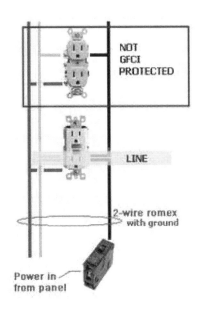

NOT GFCI PROTECTED

LINE

2-wire romex with ground

Power in from panel

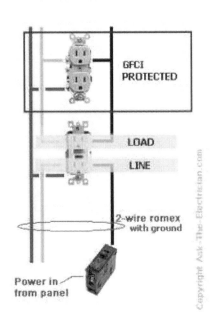

GFCI PROTECTED

LOAD

LINE

2-wire romex with ground

Power in from panel

Copyright Ask-The-Electrician.com

Light Switches

Single Pole Light Switch
120 Volt 15 Amp

Light Fixtures, Ceiling Fans and
Wall Receptacles

3-Way Switch
120 Volt 15 Amp

Light Fixtures, Ceiling Fans and
Wall Receptacles

4-Way Switch
120 Volt 15 Amp

Light Fixtures, commonly used in
Hallways and Stairways

Specialty Switches

Single Pole Stack Switch
120 Volt
Standard or Decorative

Enables the use of
2 switches in a
1-Gang box

Combo Switch Outlet
120 Volt 15 Amp

Enables the use of one switch and
receptacle in a 1-Gang box

Occupancy Sensor
120 Volt 15 Amp

Bathroom or per specified code
requirement.

Dimmer Switches

**Knob Dimmer
120 Volt 600 Watt**

**Single Pole or 3-Way general
purpose dimmer switch**

**Slide Dimmer
120 Volt 600 Watt**

Single Pole Dimmer with a pre-set switch

**120 Volt 600 Watt Dimmer and
Ceiling Fan Speed Control**

**Combo Switch, two functions
from a single gang switch**

**Large Dimmer
120 Volt 800 Watt and higher
capacity**

**For lighting circuits with
multiple fixtures and lamps**

Timer Switches and Lighting Controls

Programmable Lighting Control with Digital Display

Great for outdoor lighting, such as porch lights, walkway or driveway.

Spring Wound Time Control

Specific device use, such as exhaust fan or bathroom heat lamp.

Time Switch

Great for outdoor lighting, such as porch lights, walkway or driveway.

Time Clock Control Available in 120 and 240 Volt

Control one or two circuits, for lighting or pump motors.

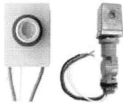

Photo Cell Controls Internal or External Unit

Control one or more light fixtures, load specific ranges available.
Ideal when used with a time clock as an optimal lighting control.

Typical Time Control Wiring Connections:
LINE - Power Source: Black-Power, White-Neutral
LOAD - Power to the Fixture: Red
Note: Some time controls require a neutral on the line side for operation. Time clocks and home automation wiring are specific to each brand and type.

Light Fixture Hardware

Wall mounted light fixture adapter. For fixtures with two threaded mounting studs with decorative fastening nuts. Required when the fixture needs to be rotated or leveled.

Wall or ceiling mounted light fixture adapter. For fixtures with two threaded mounting studs with decorative fastening nuts.

Wall or ceiling mounted light fixture adapter. For fixtures with a threaded stem mount and fastening nut.

Wall or ceiling mounted light fixture adapter. For fixtures with two threaded mounting studs with decorative fastening nuts. Required when the fixture needs to be rotated or leveled.

Support hook for heavy light fixtures. Requires a special light fixture box. All mounting hardware for heavy light fixtures must be rated for specific light fixture weight and mounting requirements.

Examples of light fixture hardware:
3/8 inch all-thread pipe, plastic bushing, nut, lock-washer, decorative washer.

Home·Electrical·Wiring

Mounting Screws and Hardware

6-32 Screws
1/2 - 3 Inch

Mounting
switches and receptacle outlets

8-32 Screws
1/2 - 3 Inch

Mounting
light fixtures

10-32 Screws
1/2 - 3 Inch

Mounting boxes, enclosures and
light fixtures

Self Tapping Tek-Screws
Square Drive

Mounting boxes and enclosures to
metal

Phillips/Square Drive
Wood Screw

Mounting boxes and enclosures to
wood

Toggle Bolt or
Aluminum Anchor

Mounting light fixtures and some
enclosures onto sheet rock ceilings
or walls

Box Fittings and Bushings

 2-Screw Clamping Cord Connector — Mounting boxes and enclosures to wood

 Snap-In Insulated Bushing — Mounting light fixtures and some enclosures onto sheet rock ceilings or walls

 Snap-In Insulated Clamping Bushing — Mounting Light Fixtures and some enclosures onto sheet rock ceilings or walls

 **Plastic Cable Connector** — 1/2 Inch

 Reducing Washers — Reduce the size of an opening of a box or enclosure

 Threaded Reducer — Reduce the threaded opening of a box or increase the size of a fitting

 Insulated Threaded Bushing — Thread onto metal fittings to protect insulated wires

 2-Piece KO Knock-Out Seals — Cover an unused opening of a box or enclosure.

 Threaded Opening Blank Seal — Cover an unused threaded opening of a box or enclosure

Electrical Code Tables

ELECTRICAL CODE TABLES

CODE TABLES

Home·Electrical·Wiring

Wire Size Ampacity Table

The wire or conductor size and type is determined by the by the specific application and the load requirement. Other considerations that will affect the wire size may be the total length of the run of wire to be installed and if the wire will be installed into conduit or in an open air environment. This table shows the amperage rating for home electrical wire sizes.

Although this is the most common table used to determine wire size, this is just one example.

Allowable Ampacity of Insulated Wire Conductors							
Wire Types	Type NM-B	60 Deg C 140 Deg F TW UF	75 Deg C 167 Deg F THHW THW THWN USE	90 Deg C 194 Deg F THHN THHW THW-2 THWN-2 XHHW XHHW-2 USE-2	60 Deg C 140 Deg F TW UF	75 Deg C 167 Deg F THHW THW THWN USE XHHW	90 Deg C 194 Deg F THHN THHW THW-2 THWN-2 USE-2 XHHW XHHW-2
Size		Copper			Aluminum		
#14	15	20	20	25	-	-	-
#12	20	25	25	30	20	20	25
#10	30	30	35	40	25	30	35
#8	40	40	50	55	30	40	45
#6	45	55	65	75	40	50	55
#4	-	70	85	95	55	65	75
#3	-	85	100	110	65	75	85
#2	-	95	115	130	75	90	100
#1	-	110	130	145	85	100	115
1/0	-	125	150	170	100	120	135
2/0	-	145	175	195	115	135	150
3/0	-	165	200	225	130	155	175
4/0	-	195	230	260	150	180	205

Circuit and Wire Size Table

Standard Over Current Devices with 75 Degree Rated Terminals

Standard Over Current Devices with 75 Degree Rated Terminals			
Circuit Size	Copper Cable NM, NM-B	Copper Cable SE, USE	Aluminum Cable SE, USE
15	#14	-	-
20	#12	#12	#12
25	#10	#12	#10
30	#10	#10	#10
35	#8	#8	#8
40	#8	#8	#8
45	#6	#8	#6
50	#6	#8	#6
55	#6	#6	#4
60	#4	#6	#4
65	#4	#6	#4
70	#4	#4	#3
75	#3	#4	#3
80	#3	#3	#2
85	#3	#3	#2
90	#2	#3	#2
100	#1	#3	#1
115	1/0	#2	1/0
120	1/0	#1	1/0

Wire Size Tables - Overcurrent Protection

Overcurrent Protection

Unless otherwise specifically permitted in the electrical code, the overcurrent protection for conductor types should not exceed the following:

Copper Conductors:
15 amps for #14 AWG, 20 amps for #12 AWG and 30 amps for #10 AWG

Aluminum and Copper Clad Conductors:
15 amps for #12 AWG and 25 amps for #10 AWG

These specifications are determined after any correction factors for ambient temperature and number of conductors have been applied.
Specific conductor insulation types are determined based on installation environmental factors such as free-air, dry or damp locations.
Although the preceding table is true and accurate, many times the wire type is not known.
There are also instances where more than one type of wire is used on a circuit. This is why it is best to use this default chart to determine the capacity of the wire sizes as listed.

Calculations for Wire Load Capacity are determined by using an 80% Load Factor.
For example:
The actual load capacity for a 20 amp #12 copper conductor would be 16 amps.
Determined by using this formula:
Amperage X .80 = Load Capacity or (20 X .80 = 16)

Remember to always check the device specifications for the required amperage and circuit breaker size, then select your home electrical wire size. Be sure to check with your local building authority for any cable restrictions.

GED - Grounding Electrode Conductor

There are a variety of grounding methods however they all require bonding together with the same size grounding electrode conductor.

GED - Grounding Electrode Conductor

The grounding electrode conductor

The size of the grounding electrode conductor shall be determined by the size of the service-entrance conductors

	Service Conductor		Ground Conductor	
	Copper	Aluminum	Copper	Aluminum
AWG	4	2	8*	6
	1	2/0	6	4
	2/0 or 3/0	4/0 or 250MCM	4	2

*The conductor that is the sole connection to a rod, pipe or plate electrode is not required to be larger than #6 AWG copper, however smaller conductors require physical protection.

Wires in Conduit Table

The number of wire conductors which may be installed into a conduit will be determined by the size of the conduit, the wire size or gauge of the conductor and the type of insulation of the conductor.

Type	Conductor	Trade Size (in.)									
THHN, THWN, THWN-2	**Size (AWG / kcmil)**	½	¾	1	1¼	1½	2	2½	3	3½	4
	14	12	22	35	61	84	138	241	364	476	608
	12	9	16	26	45	61	101	176	266	347	443
	10	5	10	16	28	38	63	111	167	219	279
	8	3	6	9	16	22	36	64	96	126	161
	6	2	4	7	12	16	26	46	69	91	116
	4	1	2	4	7	10	16	28	43	56	71
	3	1	1	3	6	8	13	24	36	47	60
	2	1	1	3	5	7	11	20	30	40	51
	1	1	1	1	4	5	8	15	22	29	37
	1/0	1	1	1	3	4	7	12	19	25	32
	2/0	0	1	1	2	3	6	10	16	20	26
	3/0	0	1	1	1	3	5	8	13	17	22
	4/0	0	1	1	1	2	4	7	11	14	18
	250	0	0	1	1	1	3	6	9	11	15
	300	0	0	1	1	1	3	5	7	10	13
	350	0	0	1	1	1	2	4	6	9	11
	400	0	0	0	1	1	1	4	6	8	10
	500	0	0	0	1	1	1	3	5	6	8
	600	0	0	0	1	1	1	2	4	5	7
	700	0	0	0	1	1	1	2	3	4	6
	750	0	0	0	0	1	1	1	3	4	5
	800	0	0	0	0	1	1	1	3	4	5
	900	0	0	0	0	1	1	1	3	3	4
	1000	0	0	0	0	1	1	1	2	3	4

Maximum Number of Conductors in EMT - Electrical Metallic Tubing

Box Fill Table

Box Fill is the number of wires that are allowed to occupy the space in an electrical enclosure. This is determined by the size of cubic inches in the usable space or area.

16 #14
14 #12
12 #10

Box Fill information is often found inside the box

Box Fill Table				
ELECTRICAL BOX EXAMPLES	Box CU. IN.	#14 Wires	#12 Wires	#10 Wires
3-INCH PANCAKE METAL	4.5	2	2	0
3-INCH CUT-IN FIBERGLASS	14.0	7	6	5
1-GANG CUT-IN FIBERGLASS	16.0	8	7	6
1-GANG CUT-IN FIBERGLASS	18.0	9	8	7
1-GANG NAIL PLASTIC	20.5	10	9	8
2-GANG CUT-IN FIBERGLASS	28.0	14	12	11
2-GLASS FACE NAIL PLASTIC	32.0	16	14	12
3-GANG CUT-IN FIBERGLASS	42.5	21	18	17
2-GANG NAIL PLASTIC	43.5	21	19	17

Underground Trench Covering

PVC conduit must be buried at least 18 deep when routed across dwelling unit property. All the service conductors of the circuit must be in the same trench or raceway. Allow the provision for earth movement (soil settlement or frost conditions) by using either S loops, flexible connections, and/or approved expansion fittings.

Minimum Covering Requirements in Trench						
SURFACE TYPE	**UF Cable**	**Rigid Pipe**	**PVC**	**GFCI 15-20 Amp**	**AFCI Circuit in EMT, PVC, ENT**	**Low Voltage 30V or Less**
General Soil	24 in.	6 in.	18 in.	12 in.	-	6 in.
Under Concrete	18 in.	6 in.	12 in.	6 in.	2 in.*	6 in.
Under a Building	1*	0	0	-	-	n/a
Concrete Slab & No Vehicles	18 in.	4 in.	4 in.	6 in.	-	6 in.
Street	24 in.	24 in.	24 in.	24 in.	-	24 in.
Driveway	18 in.	18 in.	18 in.	18 in.	-	18 in.

* **Notation**: See the applicable code for details.

Electrical Service

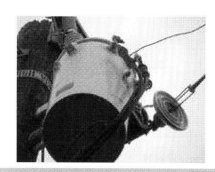

ELECTRICAL SERVICE

Electrical Service to the Home

The Commercial Electrical Distribution System

Commercial electric utility companies use several methods to produce electrical power which is then fed into "the power grid" which is then distributed to consumers using high voltage towers and sub station facilities.

High Voltage to the Transformer

Power poles provide consumer grade electricity to homes by transforming the power from high voltage to a lower voltage, most commonly 120/240 volts.

The utility company transformer is carefully sized for the amount of electricity or 'load" that will be required for one or more homes. Air conditioners are a factor when sizing the transformer.

Transformer to the Customer

This utility company power pole supplies power to a transformer which provides the customer with electricity through an underground conduit system.

The Electric Utility Service

Although the electrical contractor may be required to install part of the underground conduit system, the utility company will install and attach the main service cables or conductors to the home watt hour meter.

Recording Usage

The customer's electricity usage is recorded by a Watt hour Meter

The watt hour meter will either be an analog meter with dials and a disc, or a digital meter such as this Smart Meter.

Watt hour Meters

The analog meter records the overall usage of electricity.

Most digital meters can record real time usage information and have the capability to monitor or control specific 'smart' appliances in the home.

Alternative Energy for the Home

Alternative energy systems are becoming a very popular source of supplemental power which can actually produce more power then the home requires enabling the home to go off the grid.

The Inverter System

Alternative power sources may supply various amounts of power which becomes useable for the home with the help of an inverter.

The alternative power system must be designed to understand which components will be necessary to provide the home with the power that is required.

When alternative power is integrated into the home electrical system, disconnect devices must be installed for separation and safety.

All of the alternative electrical wiring and components must be clearly identified and labeled, along with the home electrical system.

This special watt hour meter is installed at a home where an alternative energy system has the ability to turn the meter backwards.

Depending on the type and size of the alternative power system, some homeowners may receive a refund or payment from the utility company when their energy system produces more power then is required by the home.

Electrical Codes for Photovoltaic Pg-1

✓	Location(s)	Category	Device(s)	Description
☐	photovoltaic	pv system		No multiwire or 240 Volt circuits are permitted in PV panels with a 120 Volt supply.
☐	solar photovoltaic (PV) systems	installation	back-fed circuit breakers	Plug-in type back-fed circuit breakers connected to a stand alone inverter output in either stand alone or utility-interactive systems shall be secured. Circuit breakers that are marked line and load shall not be backfed.
☐	solar photovoltaic (PV) systems	installation	AFCI direct current	Photovoltaic systems with DC source circuits, DC output circuits, or both, on or penetrating a building operating at a PV system maximum voltage of 80 volts or greater shall be protected by a listed (DC) arc-fault circuit interrupter, PV type, or other system components listed to provide equivalent protection. The PV arc-fault protection means shall comply with the following requirements: (1.) The system shall detect and interrupt arcing faults resulting from a failure in the intended continuity of a conductor, connection, module, or other system component in the DC PV source and output circuits. (2.) The system shall disable or disconnect one of the following: a. Inverters or charge controllers connected to the charge circuit when the fault is detected. b. System components within the arcing circuit. (3.) The system shall require that the disabled or disconnected equipment be manually restarted. (4) The system shall have an annunciator that provides a visual indication that the circuit interrupter has operated. This indication shall not reset automatically.

Electrical Codes for Photovoltaic Pg-2

✓	Location(s)	Category	Device(s)	Description
☐	solar photovoltaic (PV) systems	installation	open grounded conductor	A disconnect is provided between the PV power system output and other building conductors.
☐	photovoltaic	pv system		A disconnecting means is required to be on the outside or the inside nearest point of the entrance of conductors of a PV system.
☐	photovoltaic	pv system		All PV power sources require a disconnect means.
☐	photovoltaic	pv system		All PV output circuits require an in-sight disconnect.
☐	photovoltaic	pv system		A PV system with AC disconnects that are energized from 2 directions require a Warning Label.
☐	photovoltaic	pv system		A Warning Label is required at a PV DC disconnect if the terminals are hot while open.
☐	photovoltaic	pv system		A disconnect for ungrounded PV conductors must be a readily accessible switch or breaker that has no exposed live parts.
☐	solar photovoltaic (PV) systems	definition	monopole solar array	Monopole Subarray: A PV subarray that has two conductors in the output circuit, one positive (+) and one negative (-). Two monopole PV subarrays are used to form a bipolar PV array. Subarray: An electrical subset of a PV array.
☐	photovoltaic	pv system		Single conductor cable Type USE or listed and labeled as PV wire is permitted as exposed outdoor source circuits when located behind the modules.

Electrical Codes for Photovoltaic Pg-3

✓	Location(s)	Category	Device(s)	Description
☐	photovoltaic	pv system		Source circuits for a PV system are permitted in metal conduit when installed through the interior.
☐	photovoltaic	pv system		In high ambient temperature locations it is best to use 90°C wire.
☐	solar photovoltaic (PV) systems	wiring methods	PV source and output circuits	PV input and output conductors must have identification and grouping where more than one PV system exists and must be at all termination, connection, and splice points, and the means of identification must be by separate color coding, marking tape, tagging, or other approved means.
☐	solar photovoltaic (PV) systems	wiring methods	PV source and output circuits	AC and DC Conductors of more than one PV system, source circuits, output/inverter circuits that occupy the same junction box or raceway with removable cover(s), must be grouped separately by wire ties or similar means at least once, and then grouped at intervals not to exceed 6 feet.
☐	solar photovoltaic (PV) systems	wiring methods	PV source and output circuits	Source and output circuits may not occupy the same raceway, cable tray, cable, outlet box, or junction box as other non-PV systems.
☐	photovoltaic	pv system		Inverters, modules, panels, and source circuit combiners that are listed and labeled for PV systems are permitted.

Electrical Codes for Photovoltaic Pg-4

✓	Location(s)	Category	Device(s)	Description
☐	solar photovoltaic (PV) systems	installation	definition of a qualified person	Solar Photovoltaic (PV) Systems equipment installation, wiring and connections and all associated wiring and interconnections shall be installed only by qualified persons who are familiar with the construction and operation of the equipment and the hazards involved.
☐	solar photovoltaic (PV) systems	installation	circuit routing conduit	Photovoltaic source and PV output conductors, in and out of conduit, and inside of a building or structure, shall be routed along building structural members such as beams, rafters, trusses, and columns where the location of those structural members can be determined by observation. Where circuits are imbedded in built-up, laminate, or membrane roofing materials in roof areas not covered by PV modules and associated equipment, the location of circuits shall be clearly marked.
☐	solar photovoltaic (PV) systems	installation	bipolar photovoltaic systems	Where the sum, without consideration of polarity, of the PV system voltages of the two monopole subarrays exceeds the rating of the conductors and connected equipment, monopole subarrays in a bipolar PV system shall be physically separated, and the electrical output circuits from each monopole subarray shall be installed in separate raceways until connected to the inverter. The disconnecting means and overcurrent connecting devices for each monopole subarray output shall be in separate enclosures. All conductors from each monopole subarray shall be routed in the same raceway. Exception: Listed switchgear rated for the maximum voltage between circuits and containing a physical barrier separating the disconnect means for each monopole subarray shall be permitted to be used instead of disconnecting means in separate enclosures.

Electrical Codes for Photovoltaic Pg-5

✓	Location(s)	Category	Device(s)	Description
☐	solar photovoltaic (PV) systems	installation	multiple inverters	A PV system shall be permitted to have multiple utility-interactive inverters installed in or on a single building or structure. Where the inverters are remotely located from each other, a directory shall be installed at each DC PV system disconnecting means, and at the main service disconnecting means showing the locations of all AC and DC PV systems disconnecting means in the building. Exception: A directory shall not be required where all inverters and PV DC disconnecting means are grouped at the main service disconnecting means.
☐	photovoltaic	pv system		A PV system with a DC 2-wire system that is greater than 50 Volts must have a grounded conductor.
☐	photovoltaic	pv system		When a grounded conductor of a PV system is bonded to the Equipment Grounding Conductor internally within a DC GFP device, the bond is not allowed to be duplicated with an external connection.
☐	photovoltaic	pv system		Module-frames and all the metal parts of a PV system must be grounded.
☐	photovoltaic	pv system		The PV system must bond all ground-mounted array structures.
☐	photovoltaic	pv system		Equipment Grounding Conductors of the PV system must be run in the same raceway as the PV array circuit conductors.
☐	photovoltaic	pv system		Size the Equipment Grounding Conductors of the PV output circuit as per Table, no smaller than 14AWG.

Electrical Codes for Photovoltaic Pg-6

✓	Location(s)	Category	Device(s)	Description
☐	photovoltaic	pv system		The same conductor may perform the DC grounding, AC grounding, and bonding between the AC and the DC systems.
☐	photovoltaic	pv system		A PV System is required to have markings on the modules indicating the: polarity, maximum Over Current Protection Device rating for module protection, open-circuit voltage, operating voltage, maximum system voltage, operating current, short-circuit current, and maximum power.
☐	photovoltaic	pv system		A PV System must have the rated maximum currents and voltages labeled on each DC disconnect.
☐	photovoltaic	pv system		A PV system is required to have DC grounded-fault protection (DC GFP).
☐	photovoltaic	pv system		The PV System inverter must be listed as interactive if it is used in an interactive system.
☐	photovoltaic	pv system		It is permitted to feed a PV System subpanel that is isolated from the service by a transfer switch.
☐	photovoltaic	pv system		An interactive PV System must have an automatic disconnect during a grid outage.
☐	photovoltaic	pv system		For a PV System the Maximum voltage = the sum of the rated open-circuit voltage of the series-connected modules times correction factors for cold temperatures.
☐	photovoltaic	pv system		The maximum allowable voltage in a single family dwelling is 600 Volts.

Electrical Codes for Photovoltaic Pg-7

✓	Location(s)	Category	Device(s)	Description
☐	photovoltaic	pv system		For a PV System, the source circuit currents = 125% x the sum of the parallel-circuit currents.
☐	photovoltaic	pv system		For a PV System, the size of the conductors must be rated for 125% of the maximum PV source short-circuit currents.
☐	photovoltaic	pv system		For a PV System, a single Over Current Protection Device is permitted for a series-connected string
☐	photovoltaic	pv system		For a PV System, the sum of PV and main circuit breakers may not be greater than 120% of the panel rating.
☐	photovoltaic	pv system		Apply the label that warns against moving the PV circuit breaker.
☐	photovoltaic	pv system		Locate the PV circuit breaker at the opposite end of the bus from the main or feeder input.

Home Generators

Portable Generator

Stationary Generator

The connection of a generator to the home electrical system must be made using an approved method which will separate the power from the electric utility company from the power of the generator. A few of these approved methods are seen below.

Generator Circuit Panel

Allows the generator to power up a few specific circuits. Each circuit switch functions as a transfer switch.

Circuit Interlock Kit

Mechanical interlock kits are available for most panels, providing an inexpensive way to connect generator power to a panel and still provide separation from the electric utility company.

Manual Transfer Switch

This manual switch transfers the power source from the electric utility company over to the generator power source.

Automatic Transfer Switch

Permanent standby generators are often connected to the home automatically when the utility company power has been lost, and then back again when the electric utility power has been restored.

Home·Electrical·Wiring

Electrical Codes for Generators

✓	Location(s)	Category	Device(s)	Description
☐		generators		The bonding jumper may be removed if the transfer switch does not switch the neutral conductor.
☐		generators		A Grounding Electrode Conductor is required for a permanently installed generator.
☐		generators		The generator must be suitable for the environment, and rainproof if it is located outdoors and not in an approved generator shelter.
☐		generators		Generator conductors must be sized at 115% of the nameplate current rating of the generator.
☐		generators		The live or moving parts of a generator must be guarded against accidental contact.
☐		generators	transfer switches	Generator transfer equipment must prevent simultaneous connection of a generator and the electric utility service.
☐		generators	transfer switches	A sign is required at the service to indicate the generator location.

Generator Sizing Worksheets Pg-1

Generator Sizing Table
Non-Motor Loads - General Residential - Single Phase*

Electrical Circuit / Device Description	kW	120V	240V	Actual
Electric Heat (per 1000 sq. ft. home)	12	NA	50	
Heat Pump Elements (per 1000 sq. ft. home)	7	NA	29	
Electric Clothes Dryer	5.5	NA	29	
Hot Tub	10	NA	50	
Electric Range (Oven)	5	NA	21	
Stovetop Burners (each burner)	1.5	NA	6	
General Receptacles (per 1000 sq. ft. home)	1	8.3	NA	
General Lighting (per 1000 sq. ft. home)	0.75	6.3	NA	
Bathroom - Blow Dryer	1.25	10.4	NA	
Kitchen - Dishwasher	1.5	12.5	NA	
Kitchen - Microwave	1	8.3	NA	
Kitchen - Toaster	1	8.3	NA	
	Start KW	120V	240V	
Total Non-Motor Loads (this sheet)				
Total Motor Start Loads (from sheet below)				
TOTAL LOADS:				

*Guidelines Only. Check nameplate specifications for actual electrical circuit requirements.

Generator Sizing Worksheet Pg-2

Generator Sizing Table
Motor Loads - General Residential - Single Phase*

Description	HP	Run KW	Run Load (Amps)		Start KW	Start Load (Amps)	
			120V	240V		120V	240V
Refrigerator	0.5	0.5	4.9	2.5	1.5	25	13
Sump Pump	0.5	0.5	4.9	2.5	1.5	25	13
Furnace	0.5	0.5	4.9	2.5	1.5	25	13
Garage Door Opener	0.5	0.5	4.9	2.5	1.5	25	13
Freezer	0.75	0.75	7.4	3.7	2.3	38	19
Washer	0.75	0.75	7.4	3.7	2.3	38	19
Septic Grinder	0.75	0.75	7.4	3.7	2.3	38	19
Septic Lift Pump	2	2	19.6	9.8	6	100	50
Well Pump	2	2	19.6	9.8	6	100	50

*Guidelines Only. Check nameplate specifications for actual electrical circuit requirements.

Generator Panels

Transfer Switch and Circuit Panel
An all in one approach used with a standby generator to provide power to several circuits.

Generator Circuit Panel
Enables the generator to power up a few specific circuits. Each circuit switch functions as a transfer switch. Great for portable generators powering only a few specific circuits.

Generator Sub-Panel
Larger standby generators may power up a sub panel with several circuits as seen in this 125 amp rated panel.

Generator Transfer Switches

A generator transfer switch will prevent back-feeding generator power onto the electrical utility lines which could create a hazardous condition and possible electrocution for linemen who are making repairs.

Manual Transfer Switch

Automatic Transfer Switch

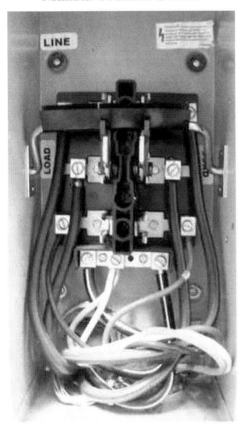

Transfer switches and wiring must be sized the same as the panel and load that is connected, however the maximum amount of available power while on generator is determined by the size and type of the generator.

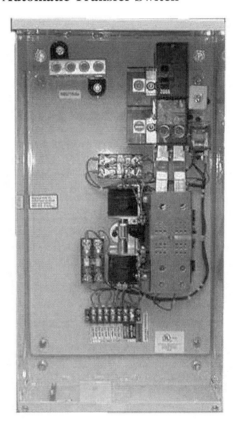

Interlock Kit installed on the main breaker and the generator circuit breaker of the existing electrical panel.

Home·Electrical·Wiring

Wiring Diagram: Generator Transfer Switch

Manual Generator Transfer Switch

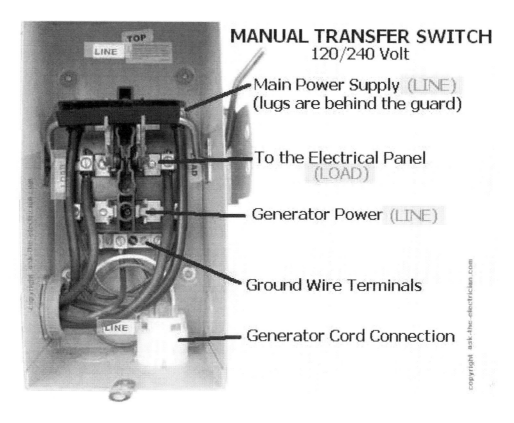

MANUAL TRANSFER SWITCH
120/240 Volt

Main Power Supply (LINE)
(lugs are behind the guard)

To the Electrical Panel
(LOAD)

Generator Power (LINE)

Ground Wire Terminals

Generator Cord Connection

Wiring Note: LINE refers to the incoming power; LOAD is the home electrical panel.

Home·Electrical·Wiring

Electrical Panels

Electrical Service Panels

Home·Electrical·Wiring

Electric Meter and Main Breaker

Most homes require a Main Service Disconnect Switch to be located outside the home near the location where the service attaches to or enters the home.

The top portion of this panel is where the cables for the main utility service will be located. This will be sealed by the utility company when the main connections have been made.

The main disconnect is especially important in the event of a fire or other emergency where the electricity should be turned off for safety reasons.

The bottom area of this panel is for the main breaker and feeder cables for a separate panel which is accessible for servicing if required.

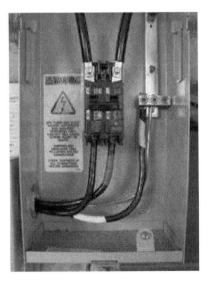

If a meter main panel is installed then it will be supplying electrical power to another panel where the circuit breakers will be located. In some areas the circuit breaker panel may be located in a basement or another accessible area of the home.

Depending on the construction or building methods, the cable leading to the circuit panel will either be the SE type or individual conductors that are installed in conduit. The method used will ensure protection for the panel feeder cables.

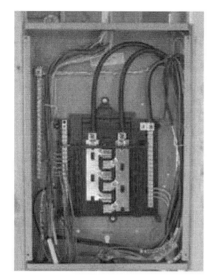

Circuit Distribution Panel or Sub Panel

The circuit distribution panel will be sized according to the size of the home and the number of circuits that will be installed.

The panel should be installed in an approved area that is accessible where the circuit wiring may be installed and maintained and free from obstacles.

Meter with Main Breaker and Circuit Distribution

This Flush Mounted 125 Amp Meter Main Service Panel is located near the garage of this new home providing easy access. The electric meter portion on the left side is sealed by the electric utility company after the main connections have been made.

The Meter Main panel with built in circuit distribution is also known as an All-In-One Panel because all three items are found in the same enclosure:
The Utility Meter, The Main Breaker, Individual Circuit Breakers.

Types of Electrical Services to the Home Pg-1

Overhead Service

The overhead service is distributed to homes from high voltage power poles where transformers are typically located.

The overhead cable, also known as Triplex, is strung between the utility power pole and the home electrical service riser.

The overhead service from the utility company makes a connection at the weather head which is mounted on top of the riser pipe which leads down to the electrical panel.

Depending on the design of the home and the location of the service panel, the riser "periscope" conduit either penetrates the roof or is located on the side of the home for the connection to the utility company.

Underground Service

The underground service may also be fed from a utility power pole or the service may be installed entirely underground.

When the utility service starts at a pole the electrical wiring is routed down the side of the pole and installed inside of conduit.

In some installations the electric utility company transformer and service connections are enclosed into a pedestal.

The electric utility company transformer or pedestal is located in the front of the home, either above the ground or in an underground vault.

Types of Electrical Services to the Home Pg-2

Selecting the Mounting Type for the Panel

Either a surface mount or flush mount panel may be installed for the home. The exact type of panel may be selected depending on the type of building construction or the personal preference of the property owner.

Flush Mounted Panel

This 200 amp flush mounted panel allows for the recessed depth to be adjusted for the finished siding material and to make sure the door has room to swing into the full open position.

This panel has an overhead service feed so a rigid conduit pipe was installed inside of the framed wall and finally penetrating the plywood sheeting of the roof.

The 125 amp flush mounted panel for this home is nicely framed with matching trim allowing it to blend in with the finished siding appearance.

This panel has an underground service so the PVC conduit was installed into the form of the foundation before the concrete was poured. The foundation or UFER Ground was installed into the foundation as well.

Surface Mounted Panel

This surface mounted panel reveals the rigid section of exposed underground conduit.

A surface mounted panel requires less preparation than a flush mounted panel for both the utility service and the incoming electrical circuit wiring.

A surface mounted meter main service panel, 200 amp, 240 volt. The stucco finished surface of this remodeled home helps hide the riser conduit and seals up around the sides of the panel.

The riser pipe or conduit for the utility service is mounted to the siding during the rough construction phase and extends to the weather head fitting above the roof.

Electrical Codes for Overhead Services Pg-1

✓	Location(s)	Category	Device(s)	Description
☐	service	definition	overhead service	The overhead conductors between the service point and the first point of connection to the service-entrance conductors at the building or other structure.
☐	feeders and services	overhead services	overhead conductor clearance	4-in-12 slope of roof must be a minimum of 3ft
☐	feeders and services	overhead services		Service conductors are generally required to be 8' above the roof but if the service conductors pass over only the overhang portion of the roof for a horizontal distance of 4' or less and terminate at a through the roof mast assembly, the clearance may be reduced to 18.
☐	feeders and services	overhead services		Vertical clearances from the edge of roof are not required to be maintained for final conductor span where the service drop is attached to the side of a building.
☐	feeders and services	overhead services	overhead conductor clearance	3 ft OK if the roof is guarded or isolated.
☐	feeders and services	overhead services	wire cable	Conductors should have a vertical clearance of not less than 8 feet above the roof surface. The vertical roof clearance above the roof level shall be maintained for a distance of not less than 3 feet in all directions from the edge of the roof. Exception No.5: Where the voltage between the conductors does not exceed 300, and the roof area is guarded or isolated, a reduction in clearance to 3 feet shall be permitted.

Electrical Codes for Overhead Services Pg-2

✓	Location(s)	Category	Device(s)	Description
☐	service entrance conductors		overhead service	The overhead raceway requires a rain tight service entrance head.
☐	jobsite panel service	temporary service overhead services	service drop	The service drop attachment may be within 24 inches when necessary.
☐	main panel service	overhead services	service drop	Point of attachment for service drop must be below the weatherhead.
☐	jobsite panel service	temporary service overhead services	service drop	The service drop must form a drip loop in each of the conductors.
☐	service entrance conductors	service equipment	overhead service	Service entrance SE cables must be sealed to prevent water entry to the box.
☐	main panel service	overhead services	feeders and services service head	Service raceways shall be equipped with a service head at the point of connection to the service drop or overhead service conductors. The service head shall be listed for use in wet locations. Exception: Type SE cables shall be permitted to be formed in a goose neck and taped with a self-sealing weather resistant thermoplastic.
☐	feeders and services	overhead services	wire cable	Conductors shall be considered outside of a building or other structure where installed in overhead service masts on the outside surface if the building traveling through the eave of that building.
☐	feeders and services	overhead services	feeders and services	Must maintain at least 3' clearance from open service conductors to openable windows, porches, balconies or similar locations.

✓	Location(s)	Category	Device(s)	Description
☐	feeders and services	overhead services	overhead conductor clearance	Vertical above decks and balconies must be 10 ft.
☐	feeders and services	overhead services		Conduit must be supported within 3' of each termination and every 10'. (Conduit extending through a roof should be secured within 3' of the point where conduit passes through the roof.)
☐		overhead service drop clearances	overhead conductor clearance	Any direction within swimming pool water must be 22 1/2 ft.
☐	overhead service drop clearances	overhead service drop clearances	overhead conductor clearance	Communications wire must be more than 12 inches parallel to power wires
☐	feeders and services	overhead services		Height of meter base is determined by local power company but is generally located 5-6' above grade.
☐	service entrance conductors	service equipment	overhead service	The minimum service entrance conductor wire size for a single family dwelling must be 4AWG CU or 2AWG AL as per Table 310-15B7

Electrical Codes for Underground Services Pg-1

✓	Location(s)	Category	Device(s)	Description
☐	service	definition	underground service	The underground conductors between the service point and the first point of connection to the service-entrance conductors in a terminal box, meter, or other enclosure, inside or outside the building wall.
☐	feeders and services	underground raceways		Direct buried cables or conductors must be protected by approved enclosures or raceways from the required burial depth or 18 in (which ever is less) to the termination point above grade or 8 feet high (which ever is less)
☐	feeders and services	underground raceways		A warning ribbon must be placed 12 inches above the conduit enclosing underground service conductors not encased in concrete and that are buried 18 inches or more below grade.
☐	feeders and services	underground raceways		PVC conduit installed above ground and subject to physical damage must be Schedule 80.
☐☐	feeders and services, detached buildings	underground raceways		Large rocks or other sharp objects may not be used to backfill trenches.
☐	feeders and services	underground raceways		Underground raceway entries must be sealed for vapor protection.
☐	feeders and services	underground raceways		An insulated bushing is required between underground cables or individual service conductors and the protective conduit.

Electrical Codes for Underground Services Pg-2

✓	Location(s)	Category	Device(s)	Description
☐	feeders and services	underground raceways		All the service conductors of the circuit must be in the same trench or raceway.
☐	feeders and services	underground raceways		Allow the provision for earth movement by (soil settlement or frost conditions) using either S loops, flexible connections, and or approved expansion fittings.
☐		cable systems	SE service entrance and underground	Type SE or USE Cable may be used as a service entrance conductor.
☐		cable systems	service entrance and underground SE	An insulated neutral conductor (type SE-R) is required except for existing dryers or existing feeders to a building with no other continuous metal path.
☐		cable systems	service entrance and underground SE	Type SE cable used for an interior installation must follow the same rules as Type NM Cable.
☐		cable systems	service entrance and underground SE	Type SE Cable is not permitted for direct burial, Type USE or Underground SE Cable is permitted direct burial.
☐		cable systems	SE service entrance and underground	Bends for Type SE Cable must be gradual and less than 5 times the cable diameter.
☐	feeders and services	underground raceways	strapping	Raceways must be secured within 3' of meter bases, panelboards, or other termination points
☐	feeders and services	underground raceways		PVC conduit must be buried at least 18 in deep when routed across dwelling unit property.

Underground Electrical Service

Electric Utility Primary Service

Underground services are becoming more popular in several areas. Most new developments restrict over head utility services all together. At a planned development most of the underground conduits are already in place and may already have the pad mounted services in place and ready to be tied into.

Types of Underground Services

Primary High Voltage	**Pad Mounted Transformer**
Secondary Voltage	**Pole Mounted Transformer**

Preparing for an Underground Service

The path which the underground conduit is to be installed must be checked to make sure other conduits or utilities are not in the same location.

Know What's Below, Call Before You Dig! CALL 811

Preparing for an Underground Service

Conduit for the primary electrical service cables must be installed according to the local utility company regulations which may include deeper trenches and wide radius 45 and 90 degree sweeps and oversized conduit. Typically Schedule 40 PVC is installed below grade. Schedule 80 PVC or rigid pipe may be required from the trench and upward.

The path of the trench must be located in an approved right of way following local building and property jurisdiction guidelines, including a possible environmental impact study.

Once the trench is dug and the conduit has been installed this phase of the installation may require an inspection by the utility company and or the local building department.

Upon approval, the conduit should be protected with a layer of sand or similar material, and once again this phase of the installation may require an inspection by the utility company and or the local building department. A warning ribbon must be placed 12 inches above the conduit enclosing the underground service conductors that are buried 18 inches or more below grade.

The final requirement for some electric utility companies is to install a pull rope. A yellow nylon rope is usually not allowed, however a flat pulling tape known as a Mule Tape or Rope is required due to its' strength and incremental measurements which make it easy to determine exactly how much cable is needed. The mule tape may be provided by the utility company and it is easily installed using a heavy duty tank or shop vacuum.

Underground Services – Pole Transformer

Pole Mounted Transformer

At locations where the home is located close to the electric utility pole, the primary high voltage is connected to a pole mounted transformer and the secondary voltage is routed down the utility pole and is connected to underground conduit which leads to the nearby home's main electrical service.

Underground Service to the Home Panel

Depending on the distance from the utility source to the home, one or more pull boxes may be required in locations as specified by the utility company. The type of pull boxes will be specified by the utility company depending on the location and vulnerabilities to damage. Molded fiberglass or concrete boxes with rated cover lids as specified.

Flanged fittings help make the installation of the cables go in smoothly and reduce the occurrence of damaged cable insulation. Additional utilities may share the same trench as long as the trench is wide enough to provide plenty of separation.

This underground main electrical panel required that a rigid pipe be installed from the trench up to the panel because the panel was located on the exterior wall of a garage where vehicles may be parked. This panel has been spaced away from the exterior siding because additional siding material was to be added later to complete the final appearance.

Underground Services – Pad Transformer

Primary High Voltage

At some locations the high voltage from the electric utility company may be extended down the pole and proceed a distance to a pad mounted transformer. This is generally done by the utility company however the trenching and conduit may be provided by the electrical contractor. The installation of this underground high voltage service enabled a remotely located home to be free of unwanted power poles.

Pad Mounted or Pedestal Transformer

Conduit to be installed by the contractor and inspected by the utility company.

Additional utilities may share the same trench as long as the trench is wide enough to provide plenty of separation. The type of pull boxes will be specified by the utility company depending on the location and vulnerabilities to damage. Molded fiberglass or concrete boxes with rated cover lids as specified.

This primary high voltage transformer pad is located several hundred feet from the utility power pole. A network of solid copper grounding conductors was also required which ultimately terminated inside the transformer cabinet.

The pre-cast transformer pad was specified by the electric utility company which provided the transformer as well as the secondary 120/240 volt service cable to the home electrical panel.

Pedestal Transformer

The underground conduit or a stub is typically provided by the utility company from the pedestal location. The pedestal transformer is typically located near the front of the home where it may supply power to more than one home. Once the main panel has passed inspection the utility company will pull in the electrical cables from the transformer to the home panel and make the primary service connections to the home panel meter base.

Underground Conduit Installation

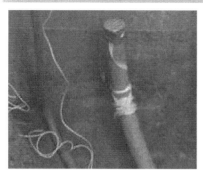

Underground Circuits

Underground conduits may be installed to provide power to equipment from outdoor lighting or electrical service for a shed or a barn.
Type USE and UF cable may be installed following the codes and guidelines.
Personally, I prefer to install PVC conduit to provide protection for the circuit conductors.

A trench will need to be dug before installing the underground circuit cables. The method you choose to install the circuit will determine the depth of the trench, and the environmental conditions of the specific project may influence the method that is used to install the circuit as well. For example if the soil conditions are hard or rocky then rigid pipe may be required.

Concrete, plastic or fiberglass boxes may be installed as pull boxes or junction boxes depending on the project or application.

When installing ground boxes make sure to support the box and provide drainage gravel or similar material. The conduits should rise above the bottom of the box to prevent being filled. Make the necessary adjustments when condensation or moisture fittings are required. Lay out the underground conduit straight and cover the ends of the conduit to prevent obstacles that may interfere with pulling in the wires or cables.

When pulling in underground cables it is helpful to use a generous amount of wire lubricant which will make the pull much easier and helps protect the cables from friction.

Electrical Codes for Sub Panels

✓	Location(s)	Category	Device(s)	Description
☐	feeders and services	subpanels		Multiple grounding conductors may be installed under the same terminal if they are the same size conductor and the maximum number of conductors does not exceed the manufacturer's instructions.
☐	panel service	subpanels, service equipment		Correct circuit breaker types must be used for each panelboard. (Example: GE circuit breakers cannot be installed in Siemens Panels.)
☐	feeders and services	subpanels, service equipment		White insulated conductors used as Hots must be identified as such at all termination points.
☐	feeders and services	subpanels		Size feeder conductors to subpanels that supply lighting and appliance loads per the calculated load and according to Table on page 58.
☐	detached buildings			The neutral conductor may not be bonded to the Equipment Ground Conductor or to the enclosure in a subpanel. A 4-wire feed is required.
☐	panelboard and cabinets	grounding and bonding		Neutrals must be isolated in subpanels.
☐	feeders and services	subpanels, service equipment		Each cable must be secured to the panelboard enclosure. (Use listed cable connectors.)
☐	feeders and services	subpanels		Main breaker not required for subpanels if over current protection is provided for feeder conductors.
☐	feeders and services	subpanels, service equipment		Each circuit must be clearly identified as to its purpose. (No two circuits may be labeled the same.)
☐	feeders and services	subpanels, service equipment		When labeling circuits, no circuit shall be identified in a manner that may be subject to potential changes in occupancy. (Example: Bill's Bedroom)
☐	feeders and services	subpanels		Bonding jumper to neutral bar must not be installed.
☐	feeders and services	subpanels		Equipment grounding bar must be bonded to the subpanel enclosure.

Sub Panels Pg-1

100 to 200 AMP Sub Panels

12 to 48 Circuits

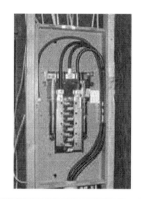

This 200 amp 120/240 volt panel was installed in a central location of the home near the kitchen which provided convenient access for the homeowner and saved on labor and material costs when installing many kitchen circuits.

This 125 amp 120/240 volt panel is installed in a separate lower level of a home which is actually used as a separate dwelling.

Although the local utility company does not allow multiple electric meters for a residence the energy consumption for this panel may be monitored and billed separately installing an energy monitor.

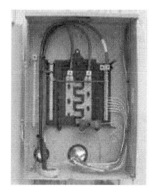

This surface mounted 125 amp 120/240 volt panel is mounted on the exterior of a workshop which is fed underground from the nearby meter main panel of the residence.

A ground rod was driven at the base of this panel.

Sub Panels Pg-2

60 to 100 AMP Sub Panels

2 to 24 Circuits

This 60 amp 120/240 volt panel is installed in an attached garage which feeds the garage lights and receptacle outlets and has additional capacity for more circuits.

This 60 amp 120/240 volt Zinsco sub-panel is installed inside a home and is being used to provide power for a large Jacuzzi Tub. Having the panel centrally located saved having to install four dedicated circuits back to a panel on the other side of the home.

Home·Electrical·Wiring

Junction Boxes and Pull Boxes

Boxes for Splicing and Pulling Cables

Above Ground Junction Boxes and Pull Boxes

Junction Box or Pull Can, Indoor and Outdoor Rated.

Wire splicing and conduit intersection.

Underground Junction Boxes and Pull Boxes

Plastic In Ground Splice Box, Junction Box or Pull Can, Indoor Rated.

Wire splicing and conduit intersection.

Concrete Splice Box and Pull Box

Junction Box or Pull Can, Outdoor Rated.

Wire splicing and conduit intersection.

Over Current Protection: Circuit Breakers

Single Pole
120 Volt

Lights
Receptacles

Single Pole Twin
Two-120 Volt Circuits

Lights
Receptacles

Double Pole
240 Volt

Dryer
Range
Stove
Water Heater
Air Conditioner

Double Pole Quad
Two-240 Volt Circuits

Dryer
Range
Stove
Water Heater
Air Conditioner

Single Pole - 120 Volt
AFCI
Arc Fault Circuit Interrupter

Bedroom Receptacles

Single Pole - 120 Volt
GFCI
Ground Fault Circuit Interrupter

Bathroom Receptacles

Double Pole - 240 Volt
GFCI
Ground Fault Circuit Interrupter

Hot Tub
Sauna

NOTE: Actual circuit breaker size may vary depending on the specific equipment load requirements.

Home·Electrical·Wiring

Electrical Codes for Circuit Breakers Pg-1

✓	Location(s)	Category	Device(s)	Description
☐		circuit breakers	aluminum wiring	Terminals including breakers must be listed and labeled for Aluminum Wire
☐	panel service	subpanels, service equipment		Correct circuit breaker types must be used for each panelboard. (Example: GE circuit breakers cannot be installed in Siemens Panels.)
☐	circuit bedroom	subpanels		All bedroom circuits must be arc-fault protected using AFCI type circuit breakers or AFCI approved receptacle device.
☐	detached buildings	panels		Must have main breaker panel, or not more than 6 circuit breakers, installed either outside the building or inside nearest the point of entrance to the building. Panelboard must be listed as suitable for use as service equipment. (Service equipment rated disconnect is not required for a single branch circuit. A general use snap switch may be used as the disconnect. Requirements are the same for service equipment.)

Electrical Codes for Circuit Breakers Pg-2

✓	Location(s)	Category	Device(s)	Description
☐	home service panel	service panel	service panel circuit breaker	Circuit breakers shall open all ungrounded conductors of the circuit both manually and automatically. Individual single-pole circuit breakers, with identified handle ties, shall be permitted as the protection for each conductor of a multiwire branch circuit.
☐	service panel	wiring methods	circuit breaker	In grounded systems, individual single-pole circuit breakers rated 120/240 volts AC, with identified handle ties, shall be permitted as the protection for each ungrounded conductor for line-to-line connected loads for single-phase circuits.
☐	panelboard and cabinets	OCPDs and wiring		Single-pole breakers with approved handle-ties are permitted for 240V circuits.
☐	panelboard and cabinets	OCPDs and wiring		Backfed circuit breakers must be secured in place.

Multi-Wire Circuits

120/240 Volt Multi-Wire Circuits

When carefully planned, multi-wire circuits can save on wiring because two circuits can share the same neutral wire if the load on the two circuits is balanced properly.

The main electrical service is a great example of a 120/240 Volt Multi-wire main circuit which shares the same neutral conductor.

A key requirement of a multi-wire circuit is a circuit breaker with a tie-bar, also known as a 2-pole breaker.

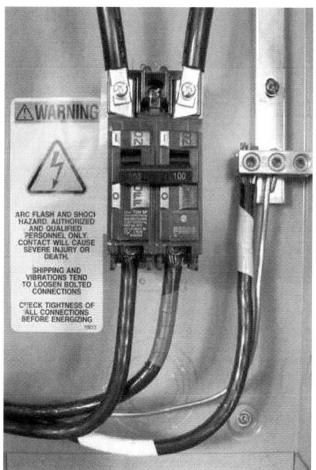

Electrical Codes for Multiwire Circuits

✓	Location(s)	Category	Device(s)	Description
☐	all	ground neutral	wiring	Neutral conductor connection of a multiwire branch circuit is not permitted to be depended on when using a wiring device such as a receptacle to maintain continuity.
☐	all	neutrals	wiring	Neutral conductor shall not be used for more than one branch circuit, for more than one multiwire branch circuit, or for more than one set of ungrounded feeder conductors unless otherwise permitted by code.
☐	panels	multiwire circuits	breaker	Each multiwire branch circuit shall be provided with a means that will simultaneously disconnect all ungrounded conductors at the point where the branch circuit originates.
☐	panelboard and cabinets	OCPDs and wiring		All the conductors of a multiwire circuit must be grouped together inside the panel using wire ties or some other method.
☐	home service panel	service panel	service panel circuit breaker	Circuit breakers shall open all ungrounded conductors of the circuit both manually and automatically. Individual single-pole circuit breakers, with identified handle ties, shall be permitted as the protection for each conductor of a multiwire branch circuit.
☐	multiwire circuits			Multiwire neutrals may not feed through receptacles or other devices (pigtail the lead from the neutral to the device in the box).
☐	temporary wiring			All temporary wiring for multiwire circuits requires handle ties.
☐	photovoltaic	pv system		No multiwire or 240 Volt circuits are permitted in PV panels with a 120 Volt supply.

Wiring Diagram: Multi-Wire Circuits

Multi-Wire Circuit
Two circuits (120/240 Volt) sharing the same neutral.

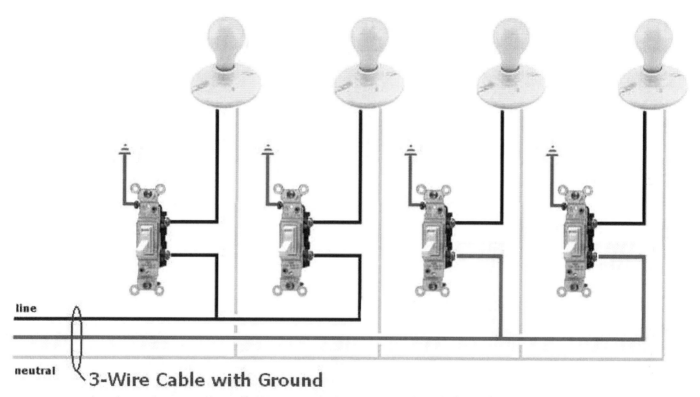

line

neutral **3-Wire Cable with Ground**

Note: Grounding is bonded through the circuit.

Safety Note: Before working on a multi-wire circuit it is important to have both circuits OFF because the shared neutral wire may be energized with return voltage if one of the multi-wire circuits is being used.

Electrical Codes for Aluminum Wire Pg-1

✓	Location(s)	Category	Device(s)	Description
☐	jobsite	temporary service	panel circuit	Service conductors must be sized according to the load but in no case smaller than #8 AWG Copper or #6 AWG Aluminum.
☐	jobsite	temporary service-underground	panel circuit	Service conductors must be sized according to the load but in no case smaller than #8 AWG Copper or #6 AWG Aluminum.
☐	service grounding	grounding electrode conductors		Metal underground gas piping or aluminum electrodes are not permitted as grounding electrodes.
☐	service grounding	grounding electrode conductors		Where used outside, aluminum grounding conductors may not be terminated within 18 inches of the earth.
☐	feeders and services	parallel wiring methods	conductors	Aluminum, copper clad aluminum, or copper conductors for each phase, polarity, neutral, or grounded circuit shall be permitted to be connected in parallel only in sizes 1/0 AWG and larger. Ex No 2: Permits 1 AWG and 2 AWG for grounded and neutral conductors.

Electrical Codes for Aluminum Wire Pg-2

✓	Location(s)	Category	Device(s)	Description
☐	panel-branch circuit	standard overcurrent device sizes - protection-non-motor appliance	35 amp circuit- #8 SE Aluminum cable	Determine Maximum Protection and Conductor Size - Current times 150%
☐	panel-branch circuit	standard overcurrent device sizes - protection-non-motor appliance	40 amp circuit- #8 SE Aluminum cable	Determine Maximum Protection and Conductor Size - Current times 150%
☐	panel-branch circuit	standard overcurrent device sizes - protection-non-motor appliance	45 amp circuit- #6 SE Aluminum cable	Determine Maximum Protection and Conductor Size - Current times 150%
☐	panel-branch circuit	standard overcurrent device sizes - protection-non-motor appliance	50 amp circuit- #6 SE Aluminum cable	Determine Maximum Protection and Conductor Size - Current times 150%

Electrical Codes for Neutrals

✓	Location(s)	Category	Device(s)	Description
☐	panelboard and cabinets	grounding and bonding		Continuity of the neutral may not depend only on the enclosures.
☐	detached buildings			The neutral conductor may not be bonded to the Equipment Ground Conductor or to the enclosure in a subpanel. A 4-wire feed is required.
☐	bonding	line-side bonding		The Service neutral may bond the line-side equipment.
☐		replacement receptacles	replacements when no grounding present	When no grounding is present in the box it is not permitted to jumper the neutral and the Equipment Grounding Conductor.
☐	equipment grounding			The neutral conductor is not to be used for grounding equipment
☐	panelboard and cabinets	locations	grounding electrode conductors	Connect to the service neutral anywhere from the service point to the bonded neutral in the enclosure of the service disconnect.
☐		generators		The bonding jumper may be removed if the transfer switch does not switch the neutral conductor.
☐	panelboard and cabinets	grounding and bonding		Neutrals must be isolated in subpanels.
☐	multiwire circuits			Multiwire neutrals may not feed through receptacles or other devices (pigtail the lead from the neutral to the device in the box).
☐		cable systems	service entrance and underground SE	An insulated neutral conductor (type SE-R) is required except for existing dryers or existing feeders to a building with no other continuous metal path.
☐		switches		A neutral wire must be provided in the switchbox

Electrical Codes for Grounds Pg-1

✓	Location(s)	Category	Device(s)	Description
☐	feeders and services	subpanels		Multiple grounding conductors may be installed under the same terminal if they are the same size conductor and the maximum number of conductors does not exceed the manufacturer's instructions.
☐	panelboard and cabinets	grounding and bonding		Continuity of the neutral may not depend only on the enclosures.
☐	jobsite	temporary service-underground	panel circuit	Service conductors must be sized according to the load but in no case smaller than #8 AWG Copper or #6 AWG Aluminum.
☐	jobsite panel service	temporary service-underground	feeders and services conduit	Underground service conductors must be protected by installation in a raceway, such as PVC conduit, Liquid Tight flexible conduit, or other approved conduit types.
☐	home service panel	service panel	service panel circuit breaker	Circuit breakers shall open all ungrounded conductors of the circuit both manually and automatically. Individual single-pole circuit breakers, with identified handle ties, shall be permitted as the protection for each conductor of a multiwire branch circuit.
☐	panelboard and cabinets	locations	grounding electrode conductors	Connect to the service neutral anywhere from the service point to the bonded neutral in the enclosure of the service disconnect.
☐	panelboard and cabinets	grounding and bonding		Neutrals must be isolated in subpanels.

Electrical Codes for Grounds Pg-2

✓	Location(s)	Category	Device(s)	Description
☐	service grounding	grounding electrode conductors		All grounding electrode conductors must be connected to the service equipment enclosure. (Main breaker panel)
☐	jobsite	temporary service	panel circuit	An 8 foot ground rod must be driven.
☐	feeders and services, grounding	service equipment	conduit connectors	Bonding bushings and jumpers are required to be used for metal conduit entering panel through concentric or eccentric knockouts, reducing washers or oversized concentric or eccentric knockouts. Standard locknuts shall not be the only means for required bonding, but shall be ensured by threaded couplings or threaded hubs, threadless couplings and connectors, or other bonding-type locknuts, bushings or bushings with bonding jumpers.
☐	service panel grounding	grounding electrode conductors	grounding	Some portion of grounding electrode conductor must be accessible at service for grounding of other systems. (Telephone or Cable TV)
☐	feeders and services	underground raceways	strapping	Raceways must be secured within 3' of meter bases, panelboards, or other termination points
☐	feeders and services	subpanels		Equipment grounding bar must be bonded to the subpanel enclosure.
☐	panelboard and cabinets	grounding and bonding		A grounding terminal bar is required if the wire Equipment Grounding Conductors are present.

Electrical Codes for Grounding Detached Buildings

✓	Location(s)	Category	Device(s)	Description
☐	detached buildings			The neutral conductor may not be bonded to the Equipment Ground Conductor or to the enclosure in a subpanel. A 4-wire feed is required.
☐	detached buildings	panels		Equipment grounding conductor must be sized based on Table.
☐	detached buildings	panels		Isolate grounds and neutrals and bond the grounding electrode conductor to the grounding bar. (Do NOT install main bonding jumper to neutral bar.)
☐	detached buildings	panels		Where there are no metallic paths from the building supplying the detached garage, 3 wires may be run to the panel. (Install bonding jumper between the neutral and ground bar and connect the grounding electrode conductor to the grounding bar. Metallic paths include metal conduit, metal water piping, etc.)

Electrical Codes for Grounding Circuits Pg-1

✓	Location(s)	Category	Device(s)	Description
☐	panels	multiwire circuits	breaker	Each multiwire branch circuit shall be provided with a means that will simultaneously disconnect all ungrounded conductors at the point where the branch circuit originates.
☐	panels	circuits	wire cable	Each ungrounded conductor of a branch circuit shall be identified by phase or line and system at all termination, connection, and splice points, and shall be identified by separate color coding, marking tape, tagging or other approved means.
☐	jobsite	temporary service-underground	panel circuit	Service conductors must be sized according to the load but in no case smaller than #8 AWG Copper or #6 AWG Aluminum.

Electrical Codes for Grounding Circuits Pg-2

✓	Location(s)	Category	Device(s)	Description
☐	home service panel	service panel	service panel circuit breaker	Circuit breakers shall open all ungrounded conductors of the circuit both manually and automatically. Individual single-pole circuit breakers, with identified handle ties, shall be permitted as the protection for each conductor of a multiwire branch circuit.
☐	service panel	wiring methods	circuit breaker	In grounded systems, individual single-pole circuit breakers rated 120/240 volts AC, with identified handle ties, shall be permitted as the protection for each ungrounded conductor for line-to-line connected loads for single-phase circuits.
☐		replacement receptacles	replacements when no grounding present	When no grounding is present in the box, a separate Equipment Grounding Conductor may be added from a receptacle box and connect to the service enclosure, Grounding Electrode Conductor, or ground bar of the panel at circuit origin.
☐	jobsite	temporary service	panel circuit	An 8 foot ground rod must be driven.

Equipment Grounding Hardware

Crimp Sleeve

Joining two or three #14 or #12 bare ground wires to form a "tail" for bonding plugs & switches

Green Grounding Screw

Bond the ground wire using tapped ground access #14 and #12 wires

Grounding Clip

For older metal boxes without a ground screw access #14 and #12 wire

Ground Lug

Bonding larger wires various sizes for wires

Ground Terminal Strip

May be installed to enclosure or panels where separation between the ground and neutral conductor is required.

Equipment Grounding Methods

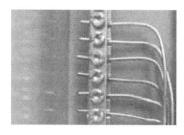

Panels

Terminal Strips are mounted and bonded to the enclosure of a main panel and sub-panel where the ground wires are terminated.

Electrical Boxes

Bond the ground wires of the cables to the boxes when a ground terminal or a ground screw may be used.

Devices

Ground all receptacles and switches that have a ground screw or terminal.

Enclosures

A ground screw may be used on most electrical enclosures and boxes.

Electrical Codes for Grounding Pg-1

✔	Location(s)	Category	Device(s)	Description
☐	service	definition	bonding termination	A device that provides a means for connecting bonding conductors for communications systems to the grounding electrode system.
☐	service grounding	grounding electrode conductors		Bonding jumpers used for bonding around concentric or eccentric knockouts must be sized base on Table.
☐	bonding	load-side bonding		Size the Grounding Electrode Conductor for water pipe bonding must be per the service wire size per Table.
☐	bonding	load-side bonding		Size the Grounding Electrode Conductor for gas pipe bonding must be per the service wire size per Table.
☐	bonding	load-side bonding		A Lightning Protection System must be bonded to the Grounding Electrode Conductor.
☐		replacement receptacles	replacements when no grounding present	When no grounding is present in the box a separate Equipment Grounding Conductor may be added from a receptacle box and connect to the service enclosure, Grounding Electrode Conductor, or ground bar of the panel at circuit origin.
☐	panelboard and cabinets	locations	grounding electrode conductors	Connect to the service neutral anywhere from the service point to the bonded neutral in the enclosure of the service disconnect.

✓	Location(s)	Category	Device(s)	Description
☐	service grounding	grounding electrode conductors		All grounding electrode conductors must be connected to the service equipment enclosure. (Main breaker panel.)
☐		generators		A Grounding Electrode Conductor is required for a permanently installed generator.
☐	grounding electrodes	concrete-encased ground electrode		A Ufer ground is not required in an existing building if concrete would have to be disturbed to gain access.
☐	service grounding	rebar in footing		All of the following grounding electrodes that are present at each building must be bonded together to form the grounding electrode system. Metal underground water piping, ground rods or pipes, rebar in footer.
☐	service grounding	metallic water piping		Metal underground water piping in direct contact with the earth for 10' or more and electrically continuous must be used as part of the grounding electrode system.
☐	service grounding	metal frame or building structure	ground	The metal frame of the building structure that is connected to the earth by at least one structural metal member that is in direct contact with the earth for 10 feet or more with or without concrete encasement, or, hold down bolts securing the structural steel column are connected to a concrete-encased electrode and is located in the support footing.

Electrical Codes for Grounding Pg-3

✓	Location(s)	Category	Device(s)	Description
☐	service grounding	concrete-encased ground electrode	ground	A concrete-encased electrode shall consist of at least 20 feet of either one or more bare or zinc galvanized or other electrically conductive coated steel reinforcing bars or rods of not less than 1/2 inch in diameter installed in one continuous length, or a bare copper conductor not smaller than 4 AWG. Metal components shall be encased by at least 2 inches of concrete and shall be located horizontally within that portion of a concrete foundation or footing that is in direct contact with the earth or within vertical foundations or structural components or members that are in direct contact with the earth.
☐	grounding electrodes	water pipe		A metal well casing that is not bonded to a metal pipe is permitted as a ground electrode.
☐	grounding electrodes			An underground gas pipe is not an approved grounding electrode.
☐	service grounding	grounding electrode conductors		Metal underground gas piping or aluminum electrodes are not permitted as grounding electrodes.

Electrical Codes for Grounding Pg-4

✓	Location(s)	Category	Device(s)	Description
☐	service grounding	ground rod pipe and plate electrodes	ground	If practical, rod, pipe, and plate electrodes shall be embedded below permanent moisture level and shall be free from nonconductive coatings such as paint or enamel. A single rod, pipe, or plate electrode shall be supplemented by an additional electrode of an approved type, and shall be permitted to be bonded to either 1.) A rod, pipe, or plate electrode, 2.) A grounding electrode conductor, 3.) Grounded service-entrance conductor, 4.) Nonflexible grounded service raceway, 5.) Any grounded service enclosure. If multiple grounding electrodes are installed, they shall not be less than 6 feet apart.
☐	grounding electrodes			The size of the electrode bonding conductors must be sized per the Ground Electrode Conductor rules.
☐	grounding electrodes	water pipe		A ground bond is required around all water meters, filters, and the like.
☐	grounding electrodes	water pipe		A water pipe cannot be the only ground electrode.
☐	grounding electrodes	pipes and rods		A ground clamp above grade is permitted if it is protected.
☐	grounding electrodes	pipes and rods		If bedrock is encountered a ground rod may be buried horizontally 2 1/2 feet deep or driven at a 45 degree angle.

Home·Electrical·Wiring

Electrical Codes for Grounding Pg-5

✓	Location(s)	Category	Device(s)	Description
☐	grounding electrodes	pipes and rods		Ground rods must be a minimum length of 8 feet in contact with soil.
☐	grounding electrodes	pipes and rods		Ground rods must be driven vertically and fully below grade.
☐	service grounding	grounding electrode conductors		Where used outside, aluminum grounding conductors may not be terminated within 18 inches of the earth.
☐	grounding electrode conductors	protection		A 6 AWG ground conductor may be unprotected if it is not subject to damage and following the building contour.
☐	grounding electrode conductors	protection		An 8AWG ground conductor must be protected by raceway or armor flex.
☐	service grounding	grounding electrode conductors		Each end of a metal raceway enclosing the Ground Electrode System must be bonded.
☐	bonding	line-side bonding		Metal Grounding Electrode Conductor enclosures must be bonded at each end.
☐	grounding electrode conductors	protection		A 6 AWG ground conductor is permitted to be unprotected if it is not subject to damage and following the building contour.
☐	grounding electrode conductors	connections		A Grounding Electrode Conductor may connect to any electrode of the Grounding Electrode System.
☐	service grounding	grounding electrode conductors	grounding	Grounding electrode conductors shall be permitted to be installed on or through framing members for installations at service equipment locations and for other than service locations.

Electrical Codes for Grounding Pg-6

✓	Location(s)	Category	Device(s)	Description
☐	service grounding	ground rods		Portion of grounding electrode conductor that is the sole connection to the rod is not required to be larger than #6 Copper. (Check with local power company. Many power companies require larger conductors.)
☐	service grounding	rebar in footing		Grounding electrode conductor that is the sole connection to rebar in the footer is not required to be larger than #4 Copper.
☐	service grounding	grounding electrode conductors, metallic water piping		Grounding electrode conductors must be sized per Table with the exception of ground rods, rebar in footer, or ground rings.
☐	grounding electrode conductors	locations		A ground conductor connection may be made to a metal water pipe that is part of the Grounding Electrode System where the connection is not greater than 5 feet after water entry to building.
☐	grounding	grounding metal water pipe and structural metal	ground	Grounding electrode conductors and bonding jumpers shall be permitted to be connected and be used to extend the connection to electrode(s) 1.) Interior metal water pipe located not more than 5 feet from the point of service to the building, 2.) The structural metal frame of a building that is directly connected to a grounding electrode by using an approved means of establishing a connection to earth.

Electrical Codes for Grounding Pg-7

✓	Location(s)	Category	Device(s)	Description
☐	bonding	intersystem bonding		Existing buildings raceway or Grounding Electrode Conductor is permitted as a bond point.
☐	service grounding	grounding electrode conductors	TV and telephone	An intersystem bonding termination for connecting intersystem bonding conductors required for other systems shall be provided external to enclosures at the service equipment or metering equipment enclosure at the disconnecting means for any additional building or structure and be accessible for connection and inspection, consist of a set of terminals, not interfere with opening the enclosure, located at the service equipment, at the disconnecting means, and the terminals shall be listed as grounding and bonding equipment.
☐	service panel grounding	grounding electrode conductors	grounding	Some portion of grounding electrode conductor must be accessible at service for grounding of other systems. (Telephone or Cable TV)
☐	bonding	intersystem bonding		A minimum 6 AWG Cu bond must connect to CATV or phone electrodes.

Electrical System Ground Bonding

Bonding the Grounding Electrode Conductors is accomplished by using the provided ground terminals and lugs within the main electrical panel enclosure and the grounding electrode conductors.

GEC - Grounding Electrode Conductors

Bonding the Ground System Within the Panel

Ground Terminal

The ground conductors may be bonded at the main grounded terminal strip inside the main panel enclosure.

Enclosure Grounding Jumper

The jumper bonds the insulated terminal strip to the enclosure. This is typically found in main circuit breaker panels where the neutral and the ground may be bonded together.

Ground Terminal Strip

The ground terminal strip on the left is mounted and bonded to the panel enclosure.
The neutral terminal strip on the right has a jumper that extends to a second neutral terminal strip within the panel.

Electrical Codes for Ground Bonding Pg-1

✓	Location(s)	Category	Device(s)	Description
☐	service	definition	bonding termination	A device that provides a means for connecting bonding conductors for communications systems to the grounding electrode system.
☐	service	definition	ground bonding jumper	The connection between the grounded service conductor and the supply-side bonding jumper, or the equipment grounding conductor, or both, at a separately derived system.
☐	panelboard and cabinets	grounding and bonding		Continuity of the neutral may not depend only on the enclosures.
☐	detached buildings			The neutral conductor may not be bonded to the Equipment Ground Conductor or to the enclosure in a subpanel. A 4-wire feed is required.
☐	service grounding	grounding electrode conductors		Bonding jumpers used for bonding around concentric or eccentric knockouts must be sized base on Table.
☐	bonding	load-side bonding		Size the Grounding Electrode Conductor for water pipe bonding must be per the Service Wire size per Table.
☐	bonding	load-side bonding		Size the Grounding Electrode Conductor for gas pipe bonding must be per the Service Wire size per Table.
☐	bonding	load-side bonding		A Lightning Protection System must be bonded to the Grounding Electrode Conductor.
☐	bonding	load-side bonding		Metal well casings must be bonded to the Equipment Grounding Conductor of the pump motor.
☐	equipment	cable systems	AC-armored cable	Armor is the Equipment Grounding Conductor - the bond wire does not enter into the box.
☐	equipment		bonding & equipment grounding methods	Nonconductive coatings must be cleaned from contact surfaces.

Electrical Codes for Ground Bonding Pg-2

✓	Location(s)	Category	Device(s)	Description
☐		replacement receptacles	replacements when grounding present in box	When grounding is present in a box bond a 3-hole receptacle to the grounded box with wire or use a grounding-type receptacle with a captive metal screw from the yoke.
☐	panelboard and cabinets	locations	grounding electrode conductors	Connect to the service neutral anywhere from the service point to the bonded neutral in the enclosure of the service disconnect.
☐	panelboard and cabinets	grounding and bonding		Neutrals must be isolated in subpanels.
☐	grounding electrodes	water pipe		A metal well casing that is not bonded to a metal pipe is permitted as a ground electrode.
☐	grounding electrodes			The size of the electrode bonding conductors must be sized per the Ground Electrode Conductor rules.
☐	service grounding	grounding electrode conductors		Each end of a metal raceway enclosing the Ground Electrode System must be bonded.
☐	bonding	line-side bonding		Metal Grounding Electrode Conductor enclosures must be bonded at each end.
☐	bonding	grounding and bonding		Bonding connections may not depend only on solder.
☐	bonding	intersystem bonding		Existing buildings raceway or Grounding Electrode Conductor is permitted as a bond point.
☐	feeders and services	subpanels		Equipment grounding bar must be bonded to the subpanel enclosure.
☐	panelboard and cabinets	grounding and bonding		A grounding terminal bar is required if the wire Equipment Grounding Conductors are present.

Electrical Codes for Grounding Service Pg-1

✔	Location(s)	Category	Device(s)	Description
☐	service	definition	ground bonding jumper	The connection between the grounded service conductor and the supply-side bonding jumper, or the equipment grounding conductor, or both, at a separately derived system.
☐	detached buildings			The neutral conductor may not be bonded to the Equipment Ground Conductor or to the enclosure in a subpanel. A 4-wire feed is required.
☐	bonding	load-side bonding		Metal well casings must be bonded to the Equipment Grounding Conductor of the pump motor.
☐	equipment		equipment grounding conductors	FMC and LFMC are permitted as Equipment Grounding Conductor for non-motor circuits in combined lengths to 6 feet with grounding fittings.
☐	equipment		equipment grounding conductors	Wire Equipment Grounding Conductors may be bare, covered, or insulated.
☐	equipment	cable systems	AC-armored cable	Armor is the Equipment Grounding Conductor - the bond wire does not enter into the box.
☐	equipment	raceways	FMC	Armor FMC is permitted as an Equipment Grounding Conductor if the fittings are listed and the circuit is less than 20 Amps, no flexibility is required, and the length is less than 6 feet long.
☐	equipment	raceways	LFMC	LFMC is permitted as an Equipment Grounding Conductor up to 6 feet if the fittings are listed, the circuit is less than 20Amps, or less than 60Amps for sizes 3/4 inch to 1 1/4 inch, and no flexibility is required.

Electrical Codes for Grounding Service Pg-2

✓	Location(s)	Category	Device(s)	Description
☐	equipment		grounding conductors	Equipment Grounding Conductor greater than 6 AWG are permitted to be stripped bare for the entire exposed length or green tape or labels may be used at the termination of the wire.
☐	equipment		grounding conductors	Insulation on Equipment Grounding Conductor may be green or green with yellow stripes.
☐	equipment		grounding conductors	The size of Equipment Grounding Conductors must be per the size in Amps of the breaker or fuse protecting circuit as per Table.
☐	equipment		bonding & grounding	Nonconductive coatings must be cleaned from contact surfaces.
☐	equipment		grounding conductors	The neutral conductor is not to be used for grounding equipment.
☐	detached buildings	wiring methods	grounding	Grounding electrode system requirements are the same as service equipment.
☐	detached buildings	panels		Equipment grounding conductor must be sized based on Table.
☐		raceways	LFMC	When using LFMC an Equipment Grounding Conductor is required.
☐	equipment		grounding conductors	The Earth is not an effective path for ground-fault current.
☐	equipment		grounding conductors	The Equipment Grounding Conductor must provide an effective ground-fault current path.
☐	feeders and services	subpanels		Equipment grounding bar must be bonded to the subpanel enclosure.
☐	panelboard and cabinets	grounding and bonding		A grounding terminal bar is required if the wire Equipment Grounding Conductors are present.

Ground Rod Installation

GEC - Grounding Electrode Conductors

Bonding the Ground of the Main Panel

Grounded Terminal Lugs

The ground conductor from the ground rod may be terminated in the main panel with the main neutral conductor.

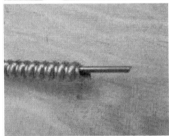

Armored Ground Conductor

The ground conductor may be required to be protected by flex or conduit in exposed areas.

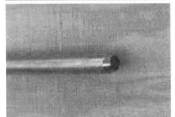

Ground Rod

This copper clad ground rod is driven to a minimum depth of 8 feet.

Acorn Ground Clamp

This acorn ground clamp bonds the ground conductor to the ground rod.

Adjustable Ground Clamp

This adjustable ground clamp has the provision for attaching the armored flex of the ground conductor.

Electrical Codes for Ground Rods Pg-1

✓	Location(s)	Category	Device(s)	Description
☐	detached buildings	wiring methods	grounding	Where the detached garage is served by only one branch circuit a grounding electrode system is not required. (1-20 amp 120 volt circuit installed for lighting and general use receptacles would not require a ground rod or connection to metal piping.)
☐	detached buildings	wiring methods	grounding	If no grounding electrode system is present at the detached structure, one must be installed. (Ground rod must be driven.)
☐	service grounding	rebar in footing		All of the following grounding electrodes that are present at each building must be bonded together to form the grounding electrode system. Metal underground water piping, ground rods or pipes, rebar in footer.
☐	jobsite	temporary service	panel circuit	An 8 foot ground rod must be driven.
☐	service grounding	ground rods		Ground rods must be at least 8' in length.
☐	service grounding	ground rod pipe and plate electrodes	ground	If practical, rod, pipe, and plate electrodes shall be embedded below permanent moisture level and shall be free from nonconductive coatings such as paint or enamel. A single rod, pipe, or plate electrode shall be supplemented by an additional electrode of an approved type, and shall be permitted to be bonded to either 1.) A rod, pipe, or plate electrode, 2.) A grounding electrode conductor, 3.) Grounded service-entrance conductor, 4.) Nonflexible grounded service raceway, 5.) Any grounded service enclosure. If multiple grounding electrodes are installed, they shall not be less than 6 feet apart.

Electrical Codes for Ground Rods Pg-2

✓	Location(s)	Category	Device(s)	Description
☐	grounding electrodes	pipes and rods		If bedrock is encountered a ground rod may be buried horizontally 2 1/2 feet deep or driven at a 45° angle.
☐	grounding electrodes	pipes and rods		Ground rods must be a minimum length of 8 feet in contact with soil.
☐	grounding electrodes	pipes and rods		Ground rods must be driven vertically and fully below grade.
☐	service grounding	ground rods		Ground rods must be driven flush with or below grade level.
☐	service grounding	ground rods		Where rock bottom is encountered at an angle up to 45°, the rod may be buried in a trench at least 30 inches deep.
☐	service grounding	ground rods		Where rock bottom is encountered, the rod may be driven at an angle not to exceed 45° from vertical.
☐	service grounding	ground rods		Portion of grounding electrode conductor that is the sole connection to the rod is not required to be larger than #6 Copper. (Check with local power company. Many power companies require larger conductors.)
☐	service grounding	grounding electrode conductors, metallic water piping		Grounding electrode conductors must be sized per Table with the exception of ground rods, rebar in footer, or ground rings.
☐	service grounding	ground rods		Connection to ground rod is not required to be accessible.
☐	service grounding	ground rods	grounding	Connection to ground rod must be made with a listed connector. (Must be listed for direct burial.)

Home·Electrical·Wiring

Foundation Bonding, Water and Gas Pipes

GEC - Grounding Electrode Conductors

Bonding the Ground Conductor to the Foundation

Foundation Bonding

Installing the main ground conductor inside the formed area for the concrete foundation with the rebar.

Ufer Foundation Ground

A continuous 20 foot length of #2 rebar is installed in this foundation and stubbed up to be accessible above the concrete where the main panel will be located.

Ufer Foundation Ground

This rebar foundation ground is stubbed up under the main panel where it is bonded and made accessible when the wall will be covered up.

Bonding the Ground to the Water and Gas

Ground Clamp for the Cold Water Pipe

This adjustable pipe clamp ground is located on the cold water pipe where it enters the home and is accessible under the house.

Ground Clamp for the Gas Pipe

This adjustable pipe clamp ground is located on the gas pipe where it enters the home and is accessible inside the garage ceiling.

Electrical Codes for Grounding Water Pipes

✓	Location(s)	Category	Device(s)	Description
☐	detached buildings			The exception is existing installations to separate structures that do not have continuous metal paths, such as a metal water pipe, between the structures.
☐	bonding	load-side bonding		Size the Grounding Electrode Conductor for water pipe bonding must be per the service wire size per Table.
☐	bonding	load-side bonding		Bond any metal piping system that is capable of becoming energized, including the hot and cold water pipe and the gas pipe.
☐	grounding electrodes	water pipe		A metal well casing that is not bonded to a metal pipe is permitted as a ground electrode.
☐	grounding electrodes	water pipe		A ground bond is required around all water meters, filters, and the like.
☐	grounding electrodes	water pipe		A water pipe cannot be the only ground electrode.
☐	grounding electrode conductors	locations		A Ground Conductor connection may be made to a metal water pipe that is part of the Grounding Electrode System where the connection is not greater than 5 feet after water entry to building.
☐	grounding	grounding metal water pipe and structural metal	ground	Grounding electrode conductors and bonding jumpers shall be permitted to be connected and be used to extend the connection to electrode(s) 1.) Interior metal water pipe located not more than 5 feet from the point of service to the building, 2.) The structural metal frame of a building that is directly connected to a grounding electrode by using an approved means of establishing a connection to earth.
☐	service grounding	metallic water piping		Connection to water pipe must be accessible.

Electrical Codes for Grounding Outlets Pg-1

✓	Location(s)	Category	Device(s)	Description
☐	outside	wiring	GFCI receptacles	An exception is a Ground Fault Protection of equipment circuit that is dedicated to receptacles for snow-melting or deicing equipment that are not easily accessible.
☐		replacement receptacles	replacements when no grounding present	When no grounding is present in the box, a separate Equipment Grounding Conductor may be added from a receptacle box and connect to the service enclosure, Grounding Electrode Conductor, or ground bar of the panel at circuit origin.
☐	equipment grounding conductors			Replacing nongrounding receptacles must be per the requirements for the location and with an approved device using an approved method.
☐		replacement receptacles	replacements when no grounding present	When no grounding is present in the box it is not permitted to jumper the neutral and the Equipment Grounding Conductor.
☐		replacement receptacles	replacements when grounding present in box	When grounding is present in a box use a grounding-type receptacle with a captive metal screw from the yoke.
☐		replacement receptacles	replacements when grounding present in box	When grounding is present in a box bond a 3-hole receptacle to the grounded box with wire or use a grounding-type receptacle with a captive metal screw from the yoke.
☐	wiring	wire splices	connectors	Ground wire connectors, used to splice multiple grounding conductors while providing connection to switch or receptacle.

✓	Location(s)	Category	Device(s)	Description
☐		replacement receptacles	replacements when no grounding present	When no grounding is present in the box it is OK to run an Equipment Grounding Conductor separately from the circuit conductors.
☐	branch circuits	receptacles		Replacement nongrounding receptacles are not required to be tamper-resistant.
☐		replacement receptacles	replacements when grounding present in box	Replacement receptacles must be the 3-hole type if the Equipment Grounding Conductor is present in the box.
☐		replacement receptacles	replacements when no grounding present	When no grounding is present in the box a 2-hole receptacle is permitted if located in an area where a GFCI is not required.
☐		replacement receptacles	replacements when no grounding present	When no grounding is present in the box a non-grounded GFCI or GFCI-protected receptacles require a label stating No Equipment Ground.
☐		replacement receptacles	replacements when no grounding present	When no grounding is present in the box an ungrounded 3-hole receptacle that is supplied through a GFCI must also require a label stating GFCI Protected.
☐		replacement receptacles	replacements when no grounding present	When no grounding is present in the box the replacement receptacle must have GFCI protection in an area that now requires GFCI.
☐	kitchen	wiring methods common cable types	receptacles	20 Amp Breaker, 12/2 with ground NM Copper

Home·Electrical·Wiring

Electrical Codes for Grounding Switches

✓	Location(s)	Category	Device(s)	Description
☐	wiring	wire splices	connectors	Ground wire connectors, used to splice multiple grounding conductors while providing connection to switch or receptacle.
☐		switches		All switch wiring must be wired using ungrounded conductors.
☐		switches		All switch wiring must be wired using ungrounded conductors.
☐		switches		All switch wiring must be wired using ungrounded conductors except in a raceway that has sufficient room to add a neutral.
☐		switches		All switch wiring must be wired using ungrounded conductors except where the switch is not enclosed by the building finishes.
☐		switches		Replacement switches where there is no grounding means present are permitted when the faceplate is plastic or the circuit has GFCI protection.
☐		switches		Switch grounding is permitted by screws to a grounded metal box.
☐		switches		Metal faceplates must be grounded to the switch.
☐		switches		Snap switches and dimmers are required to be grounded.
☐	bathroom	wiring methods common cable types	switches	20 Amp Breaker, 12/2 with ground NM Copper
☐	dining room	wiring methods common cable types	switches	20 Amp Breaker, 12/2 with ground NM Copper
☐	kitchen	wiring methods common cable types	switches	20 Amp Breaker, 12/2 with ground NM Copper

How to Ground a Breaker Panel

Grounding Requirements for Electric Panels

Electrical wiring project guidelines are necessary to follow for most any project you may choose, and the most important component is the earth ground conductor which is bonded to the main electrical panel.

How to Ground a Breaker Panel
When Grounding an Electrical Panel the Following Apply:

- **The Main Panel**
  - The ground terminal bar is internally bonded when an external bond to earth has been installed and connected to the main panel grounding lug or grounding terminal.

- **A Sub-Panel**
  - Sub-Panels are grounded using the separate ground wire of the cable that provides the sub-feed circuit power.
  - This sub-feed cable will have 2 insulated power conductors, 1 insulated neutral conductor and one ground wire.
  - The ground wire is bonded at the main panel to the grounding system.
  - The sub-feed cable type and size will depend on the specific panel size, the application and applicable local building codes.

- **Electrical Grounding Methods In General**
  - **Grounding and Bonding**
  - All grounding electrodes that are present at each building or structure served shall be bonded together to form the grounding electrode system.
  - **Premise's Electrical Service**
  - A premise's electrical service shall be connected to a grounding electrode system consisting of a metal underground water pipe in direct contact with earth for 10 feet or more, if available on the premises, and a supplemental electrode (a rod, pipe, or plate electrode.) An additional electrode shall supplement the buried water pipe electrode.

Permits and Inspections

PERMITS and INSPECTIONS

Inspections

For the best inspection process make sure to have a good relationship with the inspector with lots of discussion and clarity to avoid unnecessary surprises.

Inspectors are usually available by telephone; call them if you have any questions.

Your local Building Department _____

Inspector's Name / Phone _____

Let me encourage you to be the best at what you do, because it will make your project so much more enjoyable.

Here's what I'm referring to:
In several locations I have developed a trust relationship with inspectors who have come to know my level of expertise and integrity, so have even gone to the point where at the time of inspection they don't inspect my work, they just ask me if everything is ok and ready for the next phase. My answer is always honest and straight forward. I have had inspectors comment on my work and state that they "wish all their jobs looked like this", wow that really makes me feel good, especially if the homeowner or general contractor is standing right there during the inspection. You too can have a reputation like that.

Staying on Track and The Importance of a Job Timeline and Communication
A good building project will have at least one person that is right on top of all of the phases of the construction process, workers and sub-contractors that are involved, key materials that are needed, and how this all fits with the over all plan and timeline for the completion of the project. This is especially true when it comes to inspections because you do not want to have an inspection if you or another trade is not ready. A failed inspection can cost the job time and money, and if the inspection was passed and someone was not quite finished with their work then they will have to hustle to get their work complete before the next phase begins, possibly the same day, and that could be a disaster.

Guidelines for the First Inspection

**Building Permit Card
and Location Guide**

A card such as this is issued from the building department, along with the permit, once the plans have been reviewed, approved, and the fees have been paid. Once the electrical panel has been installed, wired and approved the inspector will place a tag like this on the electrical panel. The local utility power company can then be notified so that power may be connected and turned on. If the project is a new home that is just starting then the power will be connected as "Temporary Power".

**Electrical
Panel
Inspection
Tag**

☐	Building permit and approved set of plans.
☐	Building permit on the card is identified; review previous inspection records and notes on the permit card.
☐	Identify the installation of electrical parts and materials.
☐	Verify that installations have been made in accordance with the instructions included in listing and labeling of materials and equipment.
☐	Verify that circuit interrupting ratings are adequate for the conditions of the installation.
☐	Verify that unused openings in enclosures have been sealed.
☐	Check for secure mounting and adequate ventilation space for equipment.
☐	Check for proper use and ratings of splices and terminations.
☐	Check temperature ratings of terminations.
☐	Verify adequate working clearances, dedicated spaces, and headroom around equipment and that a dedicated space is not used for storage.
☐	Check adequacy of entrance to and exit from working space and that working spaces have adequate illumination.
☐	Check for identification of disconnecting means and circuit directories for panel boards, switchboards, and similar equipment.

Rough-In Inspection - All Areas

- ☐ If there is any electrical wiring that is concealed before inspection, the person responsible for concealing the wiring shall be responsible for all costs resulting from uncovering and replacing the covering material.

- ☐ The installer shall schedule a final inspection when the electrical work is completed prior to the wiring being utilized and the space occupied.

- ☐ Review any previous inspection records and notes on the permit card.

- ☐ Check all the wiring methods for cable assemblies and materials.

- ☐ Check the cable installation through or parallel to framing members for proper clearance or protective steel plates.

- ☐ Verify that the correct boxes are installed in accessible locations for all junctions and outlets and pull points, and for the allowed number of conductor fill.

- ☐ Check that cables are secured to boxes and secured to framing materials.

- ☐ Check the positioning of boxes that are intended to be flush with combustible and noncombustible finished surfaces.

- ☐ Check for proper splicing devices of all equipment grounding conductors within boxes and the bonding connections to metal boxes.

- ☐ Check the equipment grounding conductors for allowed type and size.

- ☐ Check boxes that are used in floors, or intended to support ceiling fans for proper listing.

- ☐ Check recessed luminaires for clearances from combustible materials and insulation.

- ☐ Check recessed luminaries cans to be air tight or trimmed.

- ☐ Check the ground bonding of other metal pipe systems.

- ☐ Check smoke detectors for spacing, interconnected wiring and arch fault protection.

- ☐ Check fire walls for cable penetration sealing methods.

- ☐ Check support for exhaust fan boxes.

Final Inspection - All Areas

- [ ] Review any previous inspection records and notes on the permit card.

- [ ] Check for proper positioning of receptacles and faceplates, gaps around outlet boxes on walls, flush with combustible or noncombustible finished surfaces.

- [ ] Verify that conductor terminations and splicing methods are compatible with the conductor materials.

- [ ] Verify that the receptacles are bonded to metal boxes and those receptacles, switches and metal faceplates are grounded.

- [ ] Check the polarity of devices and luminaires lighting fixtures.

- [ ] Check for approved splicing devices on all equipment grounding conductors within boxes and that bonding connections to metal boxes are in place.

- [ ] Device ratings must be compatible with the circuit and equipment ratings.

- [ ] Check for the proper use of connectors and fittings and for the protection of cables.

- [ ] Check for insulated bushings or equivalent protection for cables where entering boxes and other enclosures.

- [ ] Verify that unused openings in boxes and other enclosures are sealed.

- [ ] Verify that appliances, motors, and other equipment are properly grounded.

- [ ] Installation of listed equipment must be in compliance with manufacturer's instructions.

- [ ] Fire rating of electrical assemblies must be restored at all electrical penetrations.

- [ ] Check for a disconnecting means of both permanently connected and cord-and plug-connected appliances.

- [ ] Verify that circuits for mechanical equipment have the correct conductor size and overcurrent protection circuit breaker.

- [ ] Check for arch fault branch circuits in required areas.

- [ ] All equipment and branch circuits must be labeled at all panels.

- [ ] Recessed lighting must have a gasket or caulk around the can or air tight trim.

Wiring the Home

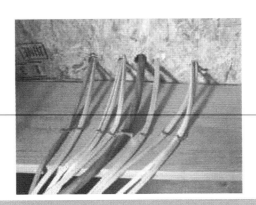

WIRING the HOME

FUNDAMENTALS

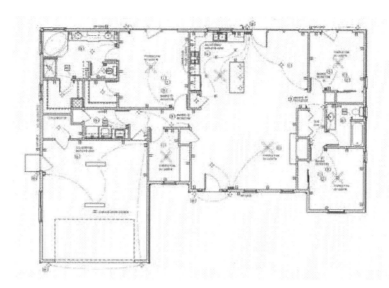

AREAS and ROOMS

THE HOME WIRNG PLAN

Wiring Methods: Overview Pg-1

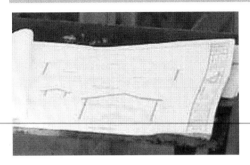

Overview of the Wiring Process

Home Circuit Wiring Methods and Materials

When I wire a home I always start with the blueprint and begin marking the studs where the boxes will be located. Then I make my measurements, fasten the boxes, and then begin drilling the holes for the Romex. You will need to examine the framing and identify any obstacles, such as plumbing or air conditioning vents. Typically the electrical wring is installed after the plumbing and the HVAC because those trades are limited to where and how they can install the materials for their systems. Electrical wiring on the other hand can be easily installed around most obstacles. Look over the structural framing to determine the path that you will take to get from the panel to each area and for any areas that may be a problem for drilling holes or installing the cables.

Home Run Cables: HR

The main cables from the panel to the first electrical junction box is known as the home run, because it is usually a non-stop length of cable running from a junction box which is the starting point of the circuit, then back to the panel. Many times the junction box where the home run is located is sized larger or deeper to provide more cubic inches, especially if this will serve as a main junction box where a GFI receptacle may be installed or a few switches. Regular sized boxes are generally used when there are only one or two 2-wire cables at the junction box; this applies to single switch boxes or outlet boxes.

Planning the Cable Path

Planning your path and identifying any obstacles will enable you to drill all the holes needed to get the cables in from point A to point B or from one junction box to the next. During the planning stage for routing the cables, you may see that some studs are grouped together or that posts were installed due to the structural framing requirements. In some cases it will be very difficult to drill through several stacked studs that are side by side, or a tight corner that will be difficult to drill through. In cases such as this it may be better to drill up and route the cable up into a ceiling area and then come back down, or drill down and route the cable down and back up to avoid structural challenges that are not drillable. In cases like this I usually choose to go up and over because it takes less time to use my ladders and install the cable then to go down stairs or under the home to install the cable and fish it back up. If the only option is to install the cable under the home then it is best to use more than one roll of cable and use each end of the roll which will enable you to stub down in more than one location and install the cables to their destination, which may be identified by using a two foot length of cable that can be inserted into the holes where each cable is to be brought up. When running cable under the home into a crawl space it is best to have a helper down below who can help to route the cable and staple it to the floor joists or bored holes where needed. When installing the cables throughout the home, it is best to use two ladders in the area you are wiring, and have a third ladder at the sub-panel location. The height of the ladders will depend on the ceiling height and your height.

Required
The Plan Set - E-Sheet
Permanent Marker, Keel or Construction Crayon
Measuring Tools for Receptacles and Switches
There are a few techniques that can be used for accurately
locating and mounting receptacle boxes:
Tape Measure
Hammer
Pre-measured block of wood
Pre-measured plywood template

Romex or Approved BX Cable
The number of rolls of Romex Cable will depend on how large the home is. 14/2: Lights and some Receptacles - 15 amp circuits, 14/3: 3-Way Switches, 12/2: Receptacles - 20 amp Circuits. Romex or Cable Staples: 1 Box of 1/2 inch 1 Box of 9/16 inch - you can always use leftovers for your second floor.

Strapping and Anchoring Cables and Conduit
Cables and conduits must be secured within 12 inches of each box and every 3 feet. When the cables and conduits are routed through interior wall studs or framing the passageway, this serves to keep the cable and conduit into position.

Protecting NM Type Cables
When NM Type cable is being installed into metal studs, insulated bushings must protect the cable. When cable or conduit enters a box, a cable or conduit connector must be used to secure and protect the cable and wiring.

Wire Connectors and Bushings
A box of each Copper Ground Crimps - large enough for 3 #12 Wires.
Yellow and Red Wire nuts.
Bushings and or cable connectors for the home runs going into the panel.
You may want to take all the cables into the panel at one time so the cover does not have to stay open. These being the case, make sure to measure the cables long enough.

Planning the Installation of Circuit Cables
Do not plan or cut cables too short. Better too long than short!

Cables, Box Locations and Cable Paths
It will be very helpful to have an understanding of the number of circuits that will be installed, the location where each home run cable will end up in its junction box or device box, and the path that the cable will take to get to that location. This will involve examining the plans, making a circuit list, and then walking through the home to carefully examine the structure materials and any obstacles.

Timeline Concern - Do Not Start Too Soon
Never begin installing any wiring into an area where all the other rough-in trades people have not completed their installation, especially the framing, plumbing, or air conditioning, otherwise you may find that your cables may need to be removed so they can install their systems.

Wiring Methods: Layout and Mark

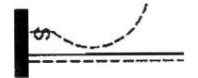

Beginning the Layout and Marking Process

Required
Set of Plans - "E-Sheet" The Electrical Layout
Permanent Marker, Keel or Construction Crayon

Receptacles and Switches
Looking at the plan of the home you will notice that the layout of the receptacles and switches are logically located and spaced and according to code when the set of plans has been produced by a licensed architect.

Wall Studs and Box Locations
When laying out an area for receptacles you can have the plan located on a sawhorse table, lay it on the floor or just carry the plan with you. The receptacle symbol may be drawn on the side of the framed stud using your marker to indicate the location. In most cases you will find that the framing of the walls does not allow the actual location of the receptacle as it is shown on the plan, so locate the receptacle as close as indicated on the plan.

Spacing the Devices
Basic spacing is within 6 feet of the door opening, and every 12 feet. If a wall section is 2 feet or greater then a receptacle must be located in that space. One way to understand the distance requirement for the placement of receptacles is to remember that electrical devices such as a vacuum cleaner typically have a 12 foot cord, so a receptacle must be located so that these devices will always have power from wherever they may be used. The spacing of these devices will depend on whether the wall is a continuous section or if there is an opening for a door. Another factor will be if the space will be treated the same as a wall, such as an area where there is an opening or short wall due to a stairway. Even if the space does not have a solid wall the area will still be treated as if there were a wall present. When there may be a decorative open stair railing and a solid wall will not be available to install the wiring then floor receptacles must be installed.

Wiring Methods: Installing Boxes Pg-1

Mount Electrical Boxes: Outlets and Switches

Time Saver and Accuracy
When using a measured block of wood for positioning outlets the process will go fast and be accurate.

Know the Wall Covering Depth
Nail boxes typically have measurement or depth marks located on the outside of the box which helps position the box so the face of the box is flush with the finished surface of the wall covering or sheet rock.

Required
Tape Measure
Claw Hammer
Pre-measured block of wood
Pre-measured plywood template

Measuring Tools for Receptacles and Switches
I have found that using the pre-measured block or 2 by 4 will be the most accurate and the fastest, especially when wiring a large custom home. I use the same method for switch boxes as well, only I use a 1 by 2. These blocks are made from straight wood that is cut straight across and marked with spray paint. The block is placed along side the front of the stud and the box is placed on top of the block resting securely ready to be nailed to the stud. Keep in mind that if you will be using a variety of boxes, they may not all have the exact outside dimensions, so when using the block of wood the height will be off slightly.

To Speed up the Receptacle Box Mounting Process
When laying out receptacles for a typical bedroom, I will gather several outlet boxes and the plan and lay the boxes next to the stud where they will be located and mounted. I will do this for two or more rooms and then go back to each room, measure and mount all of the boxes. If there may be more than two cables entering an outlet box make sure the box will be larger than 16 cubic inches to allow plenty of room for the wiring makeup and receptacle installation.

Electrical Boxes

The actual size and type of boxes that you will use will depend on the structure or framing, because you may be limited to the type of box you can install due to room or obstacles. So this will be a basic list of materials and make adjustments as needed. Please understand that I'm used to having a few rolls of each wire on hand and plenty of boxes of most varieties, so I don't expect you will be making just one trip to your supplier, in fact you may get to know the cashier on a first name basis, so just make the best of it. This job is not really big, and I may have overlooked something, so it's not a bad idea to buy extra, after all, one or two may get damaged during the process. You can choose to install fiberglass or plastic, and by all means, consult your building department for the local codes as well. In my area I can install any box with Romex cable, however up in the San Francisco area some cities require metal flex or BX cable and metal boxes. Keep in mind that the cubic inch size of the boxes will depend on the manufacturer and the type of boxes you purchase.

Typical Boxes and What They Are Used For

1-Gang Box - 16 cubic inch, mainly for receptacles and single switches.
1-Gang Deep Box - 20 cubic inch, for receptacles in locations where there will be more than two cables entering the box.
1-Gang Cut-In Box - for outside receptacles.
2-Gang Box - for switches and receptacles and switch combos at the kitchen counter tops.
3-Gang Box -for the switches in the dining room on the outside wall.
2 - 18 or 24 Inch spanner brackets with 3 or 4 inch flat boxes - for the bathroom light fixtures over the vanities.

Ceiling Fan Rated Boxes

Ceiling Fan Rated Box -This can be a flat pancake box as long as there will only be one cable coming in from the switch box, otherwise the box will need to be bigger and will depend on the ceiling structure directly above and at the location for the ceiling fan.
3-Inch Round Cut-In Box or Pancake Box - for the outside lights, the box type will depend on if there will be a stud at the location of the hole or not. I usually drill the opening for the location of the fixture then see which box I will need, a flat pancake if there is a stud, or a cut-in if the hole is open. Alternative 4 Sq Metal Bracket Box with a raised metal receptacle cover - for under the sink, dishwasher and disposal.

Wiring Methods: Drilling Pg-1

Drilling the Paths for the Electrical Cable

After the boxes have been nailed into place the drilling may begin to provide the path for the circuit cable.

Preferred Tools:

Heavy duty right angle drill with a 1/2 inch chuck.
Chip Auger Drill bits, 1/2 inch diameter and larger, 6 to 12 inches long.

CAUTION: Heavy duty drill motors are very powerful and produce a lot of torque. Protect your hands with heavy duty gloves and use the torque bar for added leverage and support. Keep the drill bits and motor away from your face.

Eye protection.
Well supported fiberglass ladders.
Heavy duty extension cord with 12 gauge wire.

NOTE: Smaller drill motors may be used for smaller projects where flat bits may be used, just try to avoid any nails.

Drilling Methods

When drilling - always look where you're drilling - even on the backside, and keep your hand out of the way of the drill bit!

Wiring Around Other Utilities

Make sure to keep a safe distance away from other systems such as HVAC ducting and plumbing. If you happen to drill into a plumbing pipe or a vent, make sure to check it out right away. A hole in a plumbing pipe can create a costly water leak. Even if it shows up during the plumbing pressure test, which could create a flood and potential damage along with some disgruntled contractors.

Drill for All Cable Paths While in One Location

During the drilling process I think about what is happening at each box location. For example, if I am at a two gang switch box I may know that there will be multiple cables that will be routed up through the top plate to supply the circuit power to another location or switched cables that will lead to light fixtures. These areas may require either a larger hole to be drilled or two or three holes to be drilled. This helps me optimize my time so I don't have to stop what I'm doing to drill another hole when I'm installing the wiring.

How to Drill a Straight Series of Holes

When drilling for the receptacles, and you're using a large half inch right angle drill or a hole hawg type drill, I have found that if you rest the drill just above your knee that you will have more leverage and maintain a good height for all the holes.

Selecting the Right Size Drill Bit

A good sharp half inch bit is fine for one cable; however I use a 9/16 bit for the majority of the holes because it is a good medium size drill bit. Sometimes I will use a larger bit for corner drilling. I typically have a short shank and a long shank drill bit for each size bit, except for the 1 1/4 and 1 1/2 diameter bits. I also use planetary bits for 1 1/2 or larger holes. For light boxes that are cut into the outside walls I use regular hole saws sized for the diameter of the electrical light box. Plumbing or pipe sizes are different than electrical boxes.

Outside Receptacles and Light Fixtures

Depending on the type of finished siding that will be installed, outside outlets and some light fixtures are generally cut in after the finished siding is in place; however these devices should be pre-wired during the rough-in wiring stage. These devices may be installed using cut-in boxes even after the interior sheet rock has been installed, but it is always best to have all the cable in place and the grounds and connections pre-made before the insulation is installed. This way if you ever have a question about making up the wiring for the switches it will be much easier to trace visible wiring while the walls are open then to use an OHM meter or tester after the walls are closed up.

Cables and Wiring

Electrical cables and conduits must be protected from damage. When installed through bored holes in joists, rafters, or wood framing members, the holes must be bored so that the edge of the hole is not less than 1 1/4 inch from the nearest edge of the wood framing member. Cables and conduits must be protected by a steel plate that is at least 1/16 inch thick and the length and width must provide a protected covering.

NOTE: Always check with local building codes to determine where holes or notches may be made in joists and other structural supports which may have some restrictions.

Wiring Methods: Installing the Wiring Pg-1

The Wiring Process

This stud reel helps electrical cable to stay flat when it is distributed off of this 250 foot roll of cable.

Wiring and Stapling the Cables

The cables need to be stapled before they enter each box so this is where I square off the cables neatly and stack them on the flat side on top of each other and align them as they run down the stud to the box, and then place a staple just above the box and then repeat the process with the remaining lengths of cable every 3 feet.

Wiring for Receptacle Outlets

Most outlet boxes have two cables which loop from one outlet to the next. To make it easier to strip the outside sheath of the NM-Type cable I will place only one cable in each of the top two entry points of the single gang outlet box.

Wiring for AFCI Circuits

For rooms such as bedrooms and other areas that require AFCI, a multi-circuit cable cannot be used because the neutral cannot be shared for AFCI so a single dedicated AFCI circuit cable is installed which may be shared for more than one bedroom, and the circuit may be 15 or 20 amps. Rarely do I install a 20 amp circuit for two bedrooms unless it is a large custom home. Typically I will put no more than 12 devices on one bedroom circuit, this includes outlets and light fixtures, however keep in mind that you should keep track of the intended circuit load as much as possible, especially with regard to light fixtures where there may be more than one light bulb installed.

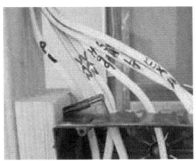

Straight Cable Runs without Loops

A nice neat cable installation is one that is straight and has no loops or kinks. The cable is kept firm but not tight which helps avoids unnecessary loops. Keep in mind that insulation may be installed into the stud bay of the wall and eventually sheet rock or other wall coverings which could pinch or damage loose cables or cables with excessive loops.

Identify Switch Wires

It is very helpful to identify the wires in multi-gang switch boxes which will save a lot of time when making up the wiring connections. I typically keep track of the circuit power wires as follows:

PI for Power In - This is the cable that supplies power to the switch box, which may be single circuit 2-wire cable or two circuits of a multi-wire circuit for larger lighting loads.

PO for Power Out - Identifies the cables that leave the box and provide power to another location.

Abbreviations are used for light fixtures or locations.

Notice that the PI cable is located closest to the stud side of the box.

Wiring for Light Switches

All light switch boxes must have a neutral wire, whether it will be used or not, so keep this in mind when installing circuit cables for lighting. The neutral wire will enable the homeowner to have more options for controlling the light fixtures.

As mentioned above, I like to identify the cables for lighting so I do not get the wires confused. The labeling can be written on the cables before they enter the box, or you may want to label them on the ends of the cables, but if you do this be careful not to cut the ends off and loose the label.

Logically installing the cables for lighting can be very helpful, and my method is to have the power cables enter the box closest to the stud side of the box, and the cables leading to the light fixtures enter the box according to how I will be arranging the switches, this helps keep the wiring in order inside the switch box preventing unnecessary clumps of wire.

Making Up the Ground Wires

If you know that there will be no additional cables added to each box, then while you are right there it saves time to go ahead and skin out the cables and remove the outer sheath and at least make up the ground wires. While you are at it you can adjust the length of the wires to at least 6 inches outside the face of the box, and make the other connections as well, such as making up all the neutral wires for the light switch boxes, and tail out the power wires and switch legs that lead up to light fixtures.

Wiring Methods: Making Up Connections Pg-1

Connecting the Wires

It is important to make up the wiring connections while the walls are open and wiring may be traced if needed. The rough-in inspection of the electrical wiring will at least require the ground wires to be made up and bonded at all electrical boxes.

Multi-Gang Switch Boxes

When more than one light switch will be installed in a box, the first switch located closest to the door opening should control the main light for the room. This will avoid confusion and provide a logical switching arrangement

Preparation for Inspection

When laying out an area for receptacles you can have the plan located on a sawhorse table, lay it on the floor or just carry the plan with you. The receptacle symbol may be drawn on the side of the framed stud using your marker to indicate the location. In most cases you will find that the framing of the walls does not allow the actual location of the receptacle as it is shown on the plan, so locate the receptacle as close as shown on the plan. When laying out receptacles for a typical bedroom, I will grab several receptacle boxes and the plan and toss the boxes onto the floor in the location where they will be mounted. I will do this for two or more rooms and then go back to each room, measure and mount the boxes.

Switch Boxes for Several Lighting Fixtures

Multi-gang switch boxes such as this one are often located at the end of a hallway and entering a living room or kitchen. The position of the switches should be logically placed for the flow of the travel from one location to the next with regard to the location of the lighting fixtures.

Testing Circuit Wiring

Looking at the plan of the home you will notice that the layout of the receptacles and switches are logically located and spaced and according to code.

Protecting the Wiring for the Next Phases of Construction

Typically the next phase of the construction process will be:

Insulation

Sheet Rock

Painting

During all of these phases of construction the electrical wiring that you just worked hard to install will be vulnerable to a few situations that could damage the wiring and cost you a lot of time and money to repair, so here are some tips to help avoid these problems:

Tuck all wires back into all boxes, do not let any wiring get close to the face of the box. This will prevent the wiring from being damaged during the dry wall or sheet rock process where routers are typically used and can damage or cut the wiring.

Insert wads of newspaper into boxes the keep the wiring from being sprayed with wall texture and paint.

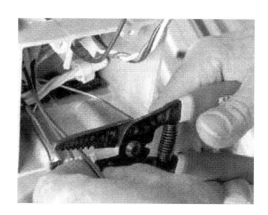

Correct Wire Stripping

Stripping wires is something that is very important and we all should pay attention to. This is why I am a strict advocate of a few guidelines that will help prevent improper wire stripping.

Guidelines for proper wire stripping:

Understand wire size or wire gauge.

The conductor that is protected by the insulation is a certain diameter, whether measured by metric or U.S. Standards. The actual conductor is based upon the electrical current it is designed for.

The importance of using the right wire stripping tools.

There have been a wide variety of wire stripping tools produced, some are great but there are a few that I would definitely advise against, especially for the novice handyman or electrician. The styles I would stay away from do not have a preset mechanism that will prevent clamping down on the wire to the point of leaving a scribed nick or impression on the conductor. The best type of electrical wire strippers are those that have a built-in stopping mechanism in place to prevent over clamping on the wire conductor size that is identified on the wire stripping tool.

The importance of removing the correct length of insulation.

Most electrical devices including switches and receptacle outlets show a strip gage on the molding. This is the length of insulation that should be removed to make the best connection possible with the device. Stripping the wire insulation too short can produce an insecure connection and could produce an overheated area which could in time end up arcing and burning away from the connection which would produce a loss of continuity in the circuit, or a loss of power from that point on in the circuit. A wire that is stripped too long can become a hazard because it will allow the extra bare area of the conductor to be vulnerable to coming into contact with other wires such as the ground, or could become a danger to anyone who may come in contact with the wired device.

The Danger of Human Error and Judgment and Wire Stripping

Wire size

It is important to identify what wire size you are working with. All wires are required to be identified by either impression printing that is embedded onto the wire jacket or insulation of the individual wire, or an imprinted visible description onto the outer jacket or individual wire insulation. There will be other information included with this description as well.

One way to identify the wire gage is to look at the amperage of the circuit breaker and compare this to the wire table found on page 77, however you should exercise caution because there are some installations of aluminum wire, where the gage of wire is required to be larger than copper.

There is also the caution which must be taken due to other wiring which could have been installed by an unqualified person that may not be up to adopted electrical code requirements. If this is found to be the case with any wiring, the circuit should be investigated and verified to be correct.

Another way to identify the gage of the wire conductor is to examine a spare piece of the wire of the same size and using a good wire stripping tool to remove the insulation, starting with a large gage first. If the insulation does not remove freely then select the next size smaller gage. Caution must be taken to be absolutely sure you have identified the correct wire gage.

What can happen with nicks or impressions on wire conductors?

A nick or impression could be the beginning of a breaking point when the wire is bent during handling at times such as when a receptacle outlet is having the wires attached to it, then inserting the device into the outlet box. It is possible that the nicked area of the wire conductor may break off preventing current flow or even possibly shorting with another conductor, or the conductor could make contact with the grounded box enclosure and cause a direct short to ground which would cause the circuit breaker to trip off or cause a fuse to blow. This is assuming that the circuit is properly sized and protected by the correct protection device.

So what if your wiring installation contains nicked impressions?

If your wiring installation has been installed and become nicked leading to damage causing a loss of the continuity of the circuit then this will be brought to your attention because of a fault in the circuit.

If the wiring is functioning even though there may be nicks on the wire, will this be a problem?

That is hard to say, but would depend upon the electrical loads that are placed on the circuit, and several other factors. It's better to be safe than sorry.

I am an advocate of always hiring a licensed professional electrician who performs work under the authority of the local building department or agency who will inspect the wiring project. Even if you installed wiring in your home yourself, it should fall under the guidelines of this proper procedure which will ensure that the work has been done correctly and that your electrical project will function safely.

Splicing Wires Together

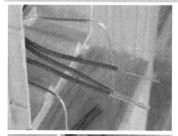

Trim and Strip

The wires should not be too long or too short. They should be cut evenly and stripped.

Place Side by Side

Align the group together and hold at the insulated base.

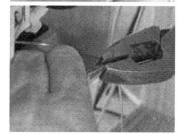

Twist Clockwise

Using lineman's pliers, twist the group firmly together.

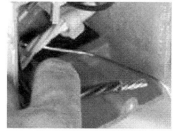

Trim Off the End

Inspect the splice and trim off the ends so they are all the same length.

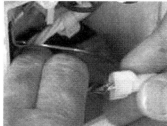

Twist on the Connector

Select the right size splice connector and screw it on until good and snug.

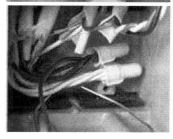

Fold and Tuck the Wires

The spliced groups will fold evenly and can be pushed to the back of the box.

Electrical Codes for Wiring Switches Pg-1

✓	Location(s)	Category	Device(s)	Description
☐	in all areas	when wiring	switches or receptacles	A switch or receptacle that has push-in backwire connections are to be made with 3/4 inch exposed conductor and inserted into the provided hole at rear of receptacle or switch provided for #14 conductors only
☐	bathroom	wiring methods	lighting	At least one wall switch controlled lighting outlet is required.
☐	bonus room	wiring methods	light outlet-switched plug	A switched light outlet is required. Lighting fixture or switched plug is acceptable.
☐	kitchen, laundry room	wiring methods	lighting	At least one wall switch controlled lighting fixture is required.
☐	living room, room occupied	wiring methods	light outlet-switched plug	A switched light outlet is required. Lighting fixture or switched plug is acceptable.
☐	garage	wiring methods	lighting	Switched lighting fixture is required on the exterior to illuminate all personnel entrances. Light fixture is not required for vehicle doors such as overhead garage doors.
☐	garage, hallway, stairwell	wiring methods	lighting	Wall switch controlled lighting outlet is required.
☐	outside	wiring methods	lighting outside	Switched lighting fixture is required on the exterior to illuminate all personnel entrances. Light fixture is not required for vehicle doors such as overhead garage doors.

Electrical Codes for Wiring Switches Pg-2

✓	Location(s)	Category	Device(s)	Description
☐	stairwell	wiring methods	lighting	Where there are 6 or more risers on the stairs, a wall switch to control the lighting outlet is required at each level. 3-way or 4-way switching is required.
☐	unfinished basement	wiring methods	lighting	A switched lighting fixture is required on the exterior to illuminate all personnel entrances. Light fixture is not required for vehicle doors such as overhead garage doors.
☐	crawl space	wiring methods	lighting	Switch for light outlet or fixture must be at the point of entrance to the space.
☐	in storage area attic areas	when wiring	lighting	Areas used for storage, such as attic spaces are required to have a switched lighting outlet or fixture.
☐	inside equipment	wiring methods	lighting	Switch for light outlet or fixture must be at the point of entrance to the space. A pull chain operated light fixture is allowed if located near the point of entry.
☐	unfinished basement	wiring methods	lighting	A wall switch controlled lighting outlet is required.
☐	wiring	wire splices	connectors	Ground wire connectors, used to splice multiple grounding conductors while providing connection to switch or receptacle.

Electrical Codes for Wiring Switches Pg-3

✓	Location(s)	Category	Device(s)	Description
☐		switches		When an AL wire will be connected the switch must be labeled CO/ALR.
☐		switches		All switch wiring must be wired using ungrounded conductors.
☐		switches		All switch wiring must be wired using ungrounded conductors.
☐	rooms & halls	wiring methods	switch 4-way	Splice neutral wires in switch boxes, do not switch neutrals.
☐		switches		All switch wiring must be wired using ungrounded conductors except in a raceway that has sufficient room to add a neutral.
☐		switches		All switch wiring must be wired using ungrounded conductors except where the switch is not enclosed by the building finishes.
☐		switches		A neutral wire must be provided in the switchbox
☐	rooms & halls	wiring methods	switch 1-pole	Switch position so on is up and off is down
☐	bathroom	wiring methods	switches	Receptacles or switches are not allowed within or directly over a tub or shower space.
☐	all	wiring methods	switches	Switches are typically mounted 48 inches from the floor to the top of the switch box but should never be higher than 6 feet 7 inches.
☐	bathroom, dining room, kitchen	wiring methods common cable types	switches	20 Amp Breaker, 12/2 with ground NM Copper

Home·Electrical·Wiring

120 Volt Receptacle Circuit Wiring

Wiring a 120 Volt Grounded Receptacle Circuit
Shown below are two wiring methods typically used when wiring multiple outlets.

Series Wiring Method	Parallel Wiring Method
Series Wiring Method	**Parallel Wiring Method**
All the circuit wiring is attached directly to the receptacle terminals or quick-connects.	The circuit wiring is spliced and only the pig-tailed wires are attached to the receptacle.

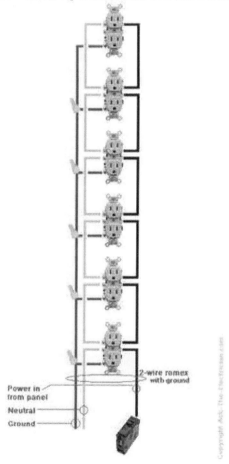

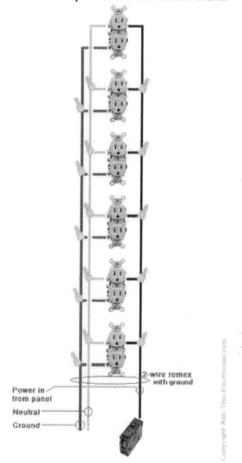

The Series wiring method makes the circuit load travel through the receptacles which could create heat and lead to loose or deteriorating wiring connections. This method is not recommended.

The Parallel wiring method uses a spliced connection where a pig-tailed wire is attached to terminals of the receptacle which will help prevent circuit breakdown.

Wiring Note: If the series wiring method is used then the failure of any receptacle may cause the rest to stop working.

✓	Location(s)	Category	Device(s)	Description
☐	all areas rooms	receptacles	tamper resistant	Tamper resistant receptacles not required if receptacles are 5 1/2 feet above the floor, are a part of luminaire light fixture or appliance, a single receptacle or a duplex receptacle for two appliances located in a dedicated space and are not easily moved, non-grounded receptacles used for replacements as permitted.
☐	bonus room, living room	wiring methods	receptacles	Receptacles outlets must be spaced so that no point along the wall is farther than 6 feet from the nearest outlet. A fireplace, doorway or similar opening is not required to be counted as wall space. Receptacles must be located within 6 feet of each side of these spaces.
☐	rooms	wiring methods	receptacles	Receptacles outlets must be spaced so that no point along the wall is farther than 6 feet from the nearest outlet. The maximum space between wall outlets is 12 feet.

✓	Location(s)	Category	Device(s)	Description
☐	bonus room	wiring methods	receptacles	Fixed panels such as the portion of a sliding glass door that is not movable must be considered wall space.
☐	bonus room	wiring methods	receptacles	Space occupied by a countertop must be counted as wall space and satisfied the requirement for placing receptacles along the wall. No point along the wall can be further than 6 feet from a receptacle.
☐	bonus room	wiring methods	receptacles	Wall space 2 feet or greater must have a receptacle outlet.
☐	living room	wiring methods	receptacles	Fixed panels such as the portion of a sliding glass door that is not movable must be considered wall space.
☐	living room	wiring methods	receptacles	Space occupied by a countertop must be counted as wall space and satisfied the requirement for placing receptacles along the wall. No point along the wall can be further than 6 feet from a receptacle.
☐	living room	wiring methods	receptacles	Wall space 2 feet or greater must have a receptacle outlet.
☐	rooms	wiring methods	receptacles	A wall space shall include any space 2 feet or more in width, including space measured around corners, and unbroken along the floor line by doorways and similar openings, fireplaces, and fixed cabinets.
☐	rooms	wiring methods	receptacles	Fixed railings must be counted as wall space. If no area is available for wall mounted receptacles, listed floor boxes and covers must be used.
☐	rooms	wiring methods	receptacles	Wall space 2 feet or greater must have a receptacle outlet.

Electrical Codes for Wiring Receptacles Pg-3

✓	Location(s)	Category	Device(s)	Description
☐	bonus room, living room	wiring methods	receptacles	If a wall space is not available, receptacles must be installed on the floor. Receptacles installed on the floor must be within 18 inches of the wall to be counted as a required receptacle. Floor boxes and covers must be listed for floor use.
☐	rooms	wiring methods	receptacles	Receptacles may be mounted at any height but may not be counted as required outlets if located more than 5 feet 6 inches above the floor.
☐	room	wiring methods	ceiling fan, lighting fixture	From panelboard or receptacle, power supply with 2-conductor with ground NM cable 120 volt.
☐	bonus room, living room, rooms	receptacles	tamper resistant receptacles	All 125-volt, 15- and 20- amp receptacles installed in dwelling units shall be listed tamper-resistant.
☐	dining room	wiring methods common cable types	receptacles	20 Amp Breaker, 12/2 with ground NM Copper.
☐	bedroom living room family room living-area	wiring methods and common cable type	lights and receptacles circuit wiring	14/2 with ground NM Copper, 15 Amp Breaker.

Electrical Codes for Wiring Appliances Pg-1

✓	Location(s)	Category	Device(s)	Description
☐		appliances	air-conditioning	A working space is required in front of an air conditioning disconnect switch.
☐	all areas rooms	receptacles	tamper resistant	Tamper resistant receptacles not required if receptacles are 5 1/2 feet above the floor, are a part of luminaire light fixture or appliance, a single receptacle or a duplex receptacle for two appliances located in a dedicated space and are not easily moved, non-grounded receptacles used for replacements as permitted.
☐	home	appliances	carbon monoxide alarms	Carbon Monoxide Alarms are required outside sleeping areas in dwellings with fuel-fired appliances or with attached garages.
☐	home	appliances	carbon monoxide alarms	Carbon Monoxide Alarms are required when remodeling where a permit is required.
☐	home	appliances	carbon monoxide alarms	Carbon Monoxide Alarms must be installed according to manufacturer's instructions and in compliance with UL 2034.

Electrical Codes for Wiring Appliances Pg-2

✓	Location(s)	Category	Device(s)	Description
☐		appliances	disconnecting devices	Cord connected appliances are required to have an attachment plug.
☐	central furnace	appliances		The central furnace system includes all associated equipment (electrostatic filters, pumps, etc).
☐	central furnace	appliances		The central furnace must be on an individual circuit.
☐		appliances	central vacuum	Bond all non-current-carrying metal parts of a central vacuum system.
☐	kitchen	appliances		Cords are permitted on kitchen appliances that are listed for the same purpose.
☐	kitchen	appliances		Cord and plug ovens and cooking units are permitted if they are listed and labeled.
☐		appliances	disconnecting devices	A circuit breaker alone is permitted as the disconnect means for appliances that are less than 300VA or 1/8 hp.
☐		appliances	disconnecting devices	Appliances that are 300VA or greater or 1/8 hp must have an in-sight switch or circuit breaker, or a lockable circuit breaker is permitted when it is not in sight.
☐		appliances	disconnecting devices	An appliance is permitted to have an accessible attachment plug as a means of disconnect.
☐		appliances	disconnecting devices	An appliance is required to have an additional disconnect if the plug not accessible.

Electrical Codes for Wiring Appliances Pg-3

✔	Location(s)	Category	Device(s)	Description
☐		appliances	disconnecting devices	Unit switch opening all ungrounded conductors OK
☐		appliances	disconnecting devices	All appliances are required to have a disconnecting means.
☐		appliances	electric furnaces and space heaters	An appliance unit switch that opens all ungrounded conductors is permitted as a disconnect for a space heater with a motor that is not greater than 1/8 hp.
☐	rooms	appliances	electric furnaces and space heaters	An appliance disconnect means must be in sight or there must be a lockable circuit breaker.
☐		appliances	hydro-massage tub	Disconnecting means required in sight of motor
☐		appliances	air-conditioning	The Circuit Wiring and Over Current Protection Device must be rated per the nameplate of the listed and labeled equipment.
☐		appliances	air-conditioning	A room air conditioning plug disconnect is permitted if it controls 6 feet or less of floor.
☐		appliances	air-conditioning	Max cord length for air conditioners is 10 feet for a 120 volt unit and 6 feet for a 240 volt unit.
☐		appliances	air-conditioning	AFCI or LCDI (leakage current detection interrupter) must be provided in the cord or the plug for room air conditioner units.

Home Electrical Wiring Plan

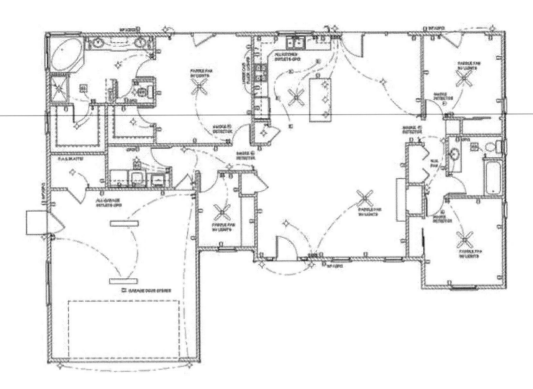

ELECTRICAL CIRCUITS

CKT#	LOAD	BRKR	LOAD / TITLE	DESCRIPTION

OPTIONS - Depending on Actual Layout:

Notes:
Check with local codes about specific requirements including: Energy Efficient Lighting, AFCI, Tamper Proof Receptacles, Smoke Detectors and Carbon Monoxide Sensors.

Kitchen Wiring Plan

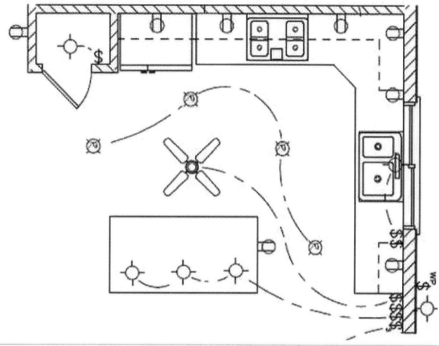

KITCHEN CIRCUITS

CKT#	LOAD	BRKR	LOAD / TITLE	DESCRIPTION
		1P-20	Appliance Circuit #1	Countertop Outlets, GFCI Protected
		1P-20	Appliance Circuit #2	Countertop Outlets, GFCI Protected
		1P-20	Dishwasher and Disposal	Under sink, toward dishwasher
		1P-15	Refrigerator	Behind refer, high for easy access
		1P-15	Lighting, Ceiling Fan	Passage, Countertop, Cabinets
		2P-50	Freestanding Range	
OPTIONS - Depending on Actual Preferences:				
		2P-40	Cooktop Drop-In Stove	
		2P-30	Oven	
		1P-20	Microwave/Micro Ex. Combo.	Counter or cabinet at Hood Ex. Fan
		1P-20	Warming Tray	Cabinet or Island
		1P-20	Instant Hot Water Dispenser	Under sink

Notes: Hood exhaust fan may be fed from countertop outlet circuit. Island receptacles may be branched off of an appliance circuit. Telephone or Intercom service.

Kitchen Electrical Code Basics

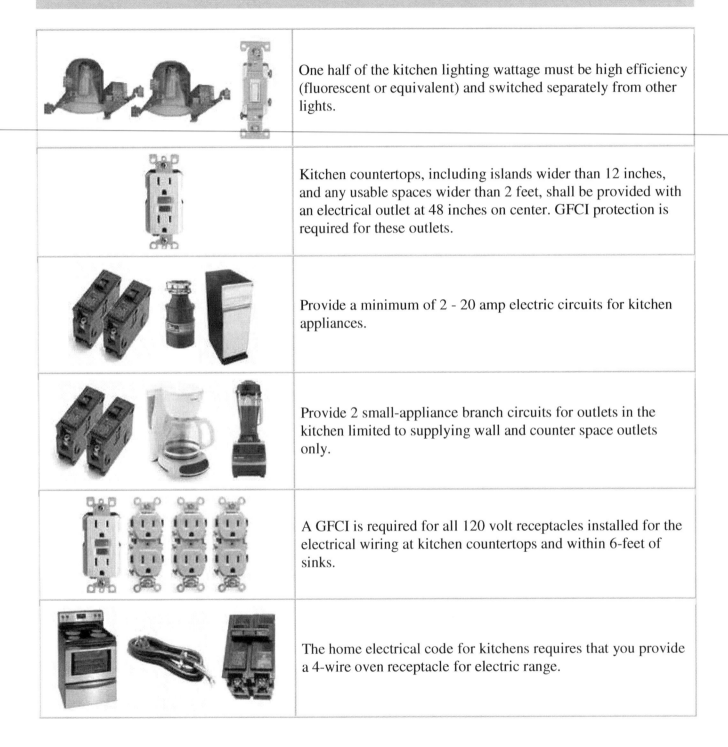

	One half of the kitchen lighting wattage must be high efficiency (fluorescent or equivalent) and switched separately from other lights.
	Kitchen countertops, including islands wider than 12 inches, and any usable spaces wider than 2 feet, shall be provided with an electrical outlet at 48 inches on center. GFCI protection is required for these outlets.
	Provide a minimum of 2 - 20 amp electric circuits for kitchen appliances.
	Provide 2 small-appliance branch circuits for outlets in the kitchen limited to supplying wall and counter space outlets only.
	A GFCI is required for all 120 volt receptacles installed for the electrical wiring at kitchen countertops and within 6-feet of sinks.
	The home electrical code for kitchens requires that you provide a 4-wire oven receptacle for electric range.

Electrical Codes for Kitchen Small Appliance

✓	Location(s)	Category	Device(s)	Description
☐	kitchen	branch circuits		No other outlets (including lights) on small appliance branch circuits
☐	kitchen	wiring methods	AFCI outlet circuit	AFCI protected receptacles are not required in kitchens
☐	kitchen		receptacles	Switched receptacles installed as required lighting do not count as part of required receptacle outlets unless half hot
☐	kitchen		receptacles	Receptacles that are part of electrical baseboard heaters Ok as required outlets
☐	kitchen		receptacles	Receptacles >5 1/2 ft. high not OK as required outlets
☐	rooms, kitchen	wiring methods	receptacles	Receptacles typically 48 inches above floor to top of box, no more than 20 inches above the countertop to count as a required outlet
☐	rooms, kitchen	wiring methods	countertop receptacles	Receptacle outlets shall be located on, or above, but not more than 20 inches above the countertop. Receptacle outlet assemblies listed for the application shall be permitted to be installed in countertops. Receptacle outlets rendered not readily accessible by appliances fastened in place, appliance garages, sinks, range tops, or appliances occupying dedicated space shall not be considered as these required outlets.
☐		lighting outlets		Habitable room lighting outlets may be a switched receptacle except in the kitchen.

Electrical Codes for Kitchen Wiring Pg-1

✓	Location(s)	Category	Device(s)	Description
☐	kitchen	wiring methods	receptacles	All receptacles in kitchen area must be on a 20 amp circuit.
☐	kitchen	wiring methods	AFCI outlet circuit	AFCI protected receptacles are not required in kitchens.
☐	kitchens, pantries, breakfast room, dining room	wiring methods	countertop receptacles	Receptacles installed for countertop surfaces shall not be considered as the required receptacles for the room area.
☐	kitchen	wiring methods	receptacles	No point along the wall may be further than 6 feet from a receptacle, if not counter space.
☐	kitchen	wiring methods	circuits	No other device allowed on the receptacle circuits, (such as lights or appliances). Receptacle for the refrigerator is allowed on the small appliance circuits or may be supplied from a dedicated 15 or 20 amp circuit.
☐	kitchen	wiring methods	circuits	Minimum of two 20 amp circuits required to supply kitchen counter top receptacles.
☐	kitchen cooktop	wiring methods	receptacles	If spacing behind the cooktop is 18 inches or greater, this area must be counted as wall space and receptacles must be installed so that no point along the countertop is further than 2 feet from a receptacle (or 1 receptacle every 4 feet).

Electrical Codes for Kitchen Wiring Pg-2

✓	Location(s)	Category	Device(s)	Description
☐	kitchen island	wiring methods	receptacles	An island requires a receptacle only if larger than 24 inches by 12 inches. If a sink or cooktop is installed on the island and the width of the counter behind the appliance is less than 12 inches, a receptacle must be installed on both sides. (Locate receptacle no more than 12 inches below cabinet.)
☐	kitchen peninsula	wiring methods	receptacles	A peninsula requires a receptacle only if larger than 24 inches by 12 inches. If a sink or cooktop is installed on the island and the width of the counter behind the appliance is less than 12 inches, a receptacle must be installed on both sides. (Locate receptacle no more than 12 inches below cabinet.)
☐	kitchen cooktop	wiring methods	receptacles	If spacing behind the cooktop is less than 18 inches one receptacle is required within 2 feet of each side of the cooktop.
☐	kitchen counters	wiring methods	receptacles	Counter spaces divided by range tops, refrigerators, or sinks must be considered separate spaces.
☐	kitchen sink	wiring methods	receptacles	If spacing behind the sink is less than 12 inches, one plug is required within 2 feet of each side of the sink.

Electrical Codes for Kitchen Wiring Pg-3

✓	Location(s)	Category	Device(s)	Description
☐	kitchen	wiring methods	receptacles	Island and peninsula receptacles are permitted 12 inches or less below a counter overhanging and where there is no means of installing a receptacle in an overhead cabinet.
☐	rooms, kitchen	wiring methods	countertop receptacles	Receptacle outlets shall be located on, or above, but not more than 20 inches above the countertop. Receptacle outlet assemblies listed for the application shall be permitted to be installed in countertops. Receptacle outlets rendered not readily accessible by appliances fastened in place, appliance garages, sinks, or range tops, or appliances occupying dedicated space shall not be considered as these required outlets.
☐	rooms, kitchen	wiring methods	receptacles	Receptacles typically 48 inches above floor to top of box, no more than 20 inches above the countertop to count as a required outlet.
☐	kitchen	wiring methods	lighting	At least one wall switch controlled lighting fixture is required.
☐	kitchen	wiring methods	GFCI receptacles	Receptacles installed to serve countertop surfaces must be GFCI protected. GFCI devices must be installed in a readily accessible location.

Electrical Codes for Kitchen Wiring Pg-4

✓	Location(s)	Category	Device(s)	Description
☐	kitchen	wiring methods common cable types	cooktop-30-amp	30 Amp Breaker- 10/3 with ground NM Copper 8/3 with ground SER Aluminum
☐	kitchen	wiring methods common cable types	cooktop-40-amp	40 Amp Breaker- 8/3 with ground NM Copper 6/3 with ground SER Aluminum
☐	kitchen	wiring methods common cable types	cooktop-50-amp	50 Amp Breaker- 6/3 with ground NM Copper 4/3 with ground SER Aluminum
☐	kitchen	wiring methods common cable types	dish washer/disposal	20 Amp Breaker- 12/2 with ground NM Copper
☐	kitchen	wiring methods common cable types	microwave	20 Amp Breaker- 12/2 with ground NM Copper
☐	kitchen	wiring methods common cable types	oven-30-amp	30 Amp Breaker- 10/3 with ground NM Copper 8/3 with ground SER Aluminum
☐	kitchen	wiring methods common cable types	oven-40-amp	40 Amp Breaker- 8/3 with ground NM Copper 6/3 with ground SER Aluminum
☐	kitchen	wiring methods common cable types	oven-50amp	50 Amp Breaker- 6/3 with ground NM Copper 4/3 with ground SER Aluminum

Electrical Codes for Kitchen Wiring Pg-5

✓	Location(s)	Category	Device(s)	Description
☐	kitchen	wiring methods common cable types	range-freestanding-40-amp	40 Amp Breaker- 8/3 with ground NM Copper 6/3 with ground SER Aluminum
☐	kitchen	wiring methods common cable types	range-freestanding-50-amp	50 Amp Breaker- 8/3 with ground NM Copper 6/3 with ground SER Aluminum
☐	kitchen	wiring methods common cable types	receptacles	20 Amp Breaker, 12/2 with ground NM Copper
☐	kitchen	wiring methods common cable types	refrigerator-large	20 Amp Breaker, 12/2 with ground NM Copper
☐	kitchen	wiring methods common cable types	refrigerator-standard	15 Amp Breaker, 14/2 with ground NM Copper
☐	kitchen	wiring methods common cable types	switches	20 Amp Breaker, 12/2 with ground NM Copper

Dining Room Wiring Plan

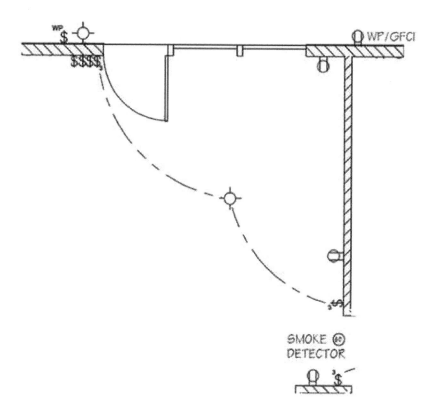

DINING ROOM				
CKT#	**LOAD**	**BRKR**	**LOAD / TITLE**	**DESCRIPTION**
		1P-15	Wall Receptacles	AFCI Protected
		1P-15	Lighting, Ceiling Fan	Passage, Countertop, Cabinets
OPTIONS - Depending on Actual Layout and Preference:				
		share	Pantry Receptacle(s)	Battery Devices Charging Station
		share	Pantry Door Jamb Light Switch	Convenience switch

Notes:
Receptacles may be fed from kitchen appliance circuit.
Lighting may be fed from kitchen lighting circuit.
Telephone or Intercom service.

Master Bedroom Wiring Plan

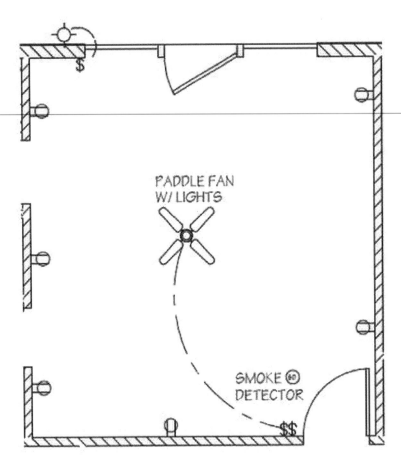

PADDLE FAN W/ LIGHTS

SMOKE DETECTOR

MASTER BEDROOM				
CKT#	LOAD	BRKR	LOAD / TITLE	DESCRIPTION
		1P-15	Wall Receptacles	AFCI Protected
		1P-15	Lighting, Ceiling Fan	Surface or Recessed Lighting
OPTIONS - Depending on Actual Layout and Preference:				
shared on circuit			Lighting	Bed Headwall or Ceiling
shared on circuit			Receptacle	Wall Mounted TV
shared on circuit			Receptacle	Gas Fireplace Insert

Notes: TV, Telephone, Intercom Service.

Master Bathroom Wiring Plan

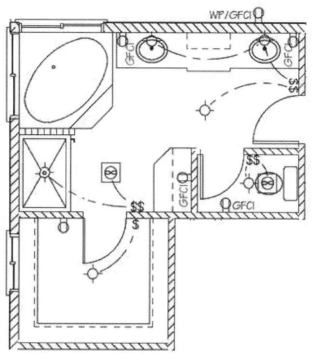

MASTER BATHROOM CIRCUITS

CKT#	LOAD	BRKR	LOAD / TITLE	DESCRIPTION
		1P-20	Vanity Receptacle	GFCI Protected
		1P-15	Vanity Light, Ceiling Lighting	GFCI Protected if over shower tub
		1P-15	Exhaust Fan and Light	GFCI Protected if over shower tub
OPTIONS - Depending on Actual Layout:				
		1P-15	Exh. Fan, Light, Heat Combo	GFCI Protected if over shower tub
		2P-20	Floor Heat System	GFCI Protected
		1P-15	Towel Warmer	GFCI Protected
		1P-20	Jacuzzi Tub	GFCI Protected
Shared GFCI Circuit			Receptacle/Plug Strip	In Vanity for Charging Devices
Shared GFCI Circuit			Receptacle/Fixture Box	Lighted Make Up Mirror
Shared Circuit			Receptacle - Walk In Closet	Burglar Alarm System above door
Shared Circuit			Receptacle - Walk In Closet	Battery Devices Charging Station

Notes: The dedicated 20 amp GFCI receptacle circuit may be used for up to five bathrooms. One GFCI protected receptacle is required for each sink. Telephone or Intercom service is optional.

Bedroom Wiring Plan

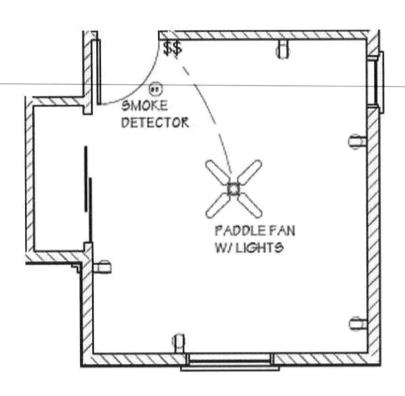

SMOKE DETECTOR

PADDLE FAN W/ LIGHTS

			BEDROOM	
CKT#	LOAD	BRKR	LOAD / TITLE	DESCRIPTION
		1P-15	Wall Receptacles	AFCI Protected
		1P-15	Lighting, Ceiling Fan	Surface or Recessed Lighting
OPTIONS - Depending on Actual Layout and Preference:				
shared on circuit			Lighting	Bed Headwall or Ceiling
shared on circuit			Receptacle	Wall Mounted TV
shared on circuit			Receptacle	Gas Fireplace Insert
Notes: TV, Telephone, Intercom Service.				

Bedroom Electrical Code Basics

	Permanently installed hardwired smoke detectors with battery backup are required in all occupied bedrooms, and in the hallway area just outside the bedroom doors.
	Arc Fault or AFCI is required for all bedroom outlet or receptacle circuits.
	Bedrooms may require tamper proof outlets or receptacles. These outlets prevent children from accessing the electrical components.
	Ceiling Fans may be installed where there is a minimum of 7 feet clearance from the floor to the fan blades.
	Incandescent lights in clothes closets need a 12 inch minimum from combustibles such as walls or the edge of shelves, measured horizontally. 6 inch horizontal clearance is allowed for recessed incandescent lights with covers or fluorescent fixtures.
	Dimmer switches may be required as an energy savings and efficiency control for lighting. Be sure that the dimmer switches and light fixture types are compatible.

Electrical Codes for Bedrooms Pg-1

✓	Location(s)	Category	Device(s)	Description
☐	dwelling unit family rooms, dining rooms, living rooms, parlors, libraries, dens, bedrooms, sunrooms, recreation rooms, closets, hallways	wiring methods	AFCI outlet circuit, individual branch circuit	It is permitted to have protection at the first outlet if the wiring method between the circuit breaker and the outlet is RMC, IMC, EMT, MC, or steel-armored cable (type AC) and if metal junction or outlet boxes are used.
☐	dwelling unit family rooms, dining rooms, living rooms, parlors, libraries, dens, bedrooms, sunrooms, recreation rooms, closets, hallways	wiring methods	AFCI outlet circuit, individual branch circuit	All 120 volt 15 and 20 amp branch circuits where the branch circuit is EMT, PVC, ENT, or other listed metal or nonmetallic conduit or tubing which is installed in not less than 2 inches of concrete for the portion of the branch circuit between the branch circuit over current device and the first outlet shall be protected by a listed arc-fault circuit interrupter at the first outlet.

Electrical Codes for Bedrooms Pg-2

✓	Location(s)	Category	Device(s)	Description
☐	dwelling unit family rooms, dining rooms, living rooms, parlors, libraries, dens, bedrooms, sunrooms, recreation rooms, closets, hallways	wiring methods	AFCI outlet circuit, individual branch circuit	All 120 volt 15 and 20 amp branch circuits supplying outlets in the required areas shall be protected by a listed AFCI arc-fault circuit interrupter, combination-type, installed to provide protection of the branch circuit.
☐	circuits dining rooms, living rooms, bedrooms, sunrooms, closets, hallways, or similar areas	subpanels	AFCI outlet circuit	All 15 and 20 amp 120 volt circuits supplying bedrooms or similar areas must be AFCI protected.
☐	bedrooms	wiring methods	AFCI outlet circuit	Arc Fault protection required for all outlets, defined by the NEC; include all lighting fixtures, smoke detectors, and receptacles.

Electrical Codes for Bedrooms Pg-3

✓	Location(s)	Category	Device(s)	Description
☐	dwelling unit family rooms, dining rooms, living rooms, parlors, libraries, dens, bedrooms, sunrooms, recreation rooms, closets, hallways	wiring methods	AFCI	Where the branch circuit wiring has been modified, replaced, or extended, the branch circuit shall be protected by a listed combination-type AFCI that is located at the origin of the branch circuit, or a listed outlet branch-circuit type AFCI located at the first receptacle outlet of the existing branch circuit.
☐	bedroom	wiring methods	smoke detector	120 volt power supply 2-wire NM with ground from AFCI protected circuit.
☐	circuit bedroom	subpanels		All bedroom circuits must be arc-fault protected using AFCI type circuit breakers or AFCI approved receptacle device.
☐	feeders and services	subpanels, service equipment		When labeling circuits, no circuit shall be identified in a manner that may be subject to potential changes in occupancy. (Example: Bill's Bedroom)
☐	bedroom living room family room living-area panel circuit	wiring methods common cable types	lights and receptacles circuit breaker	15 Amp Breaker, 14/2 with ground NM Copper
☐	laundry room bedroom living room family room living-area panel circuit	wiring methods common cable types	lights and receptacles circuit breaker	20 Amp Breaker, 12/2 with ground NM Copper

Bathroom Wiring Plan

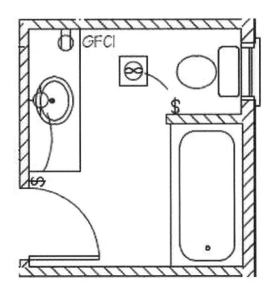

BATHROOM CIRCUITS

CKT#	LOAD	BRKR	LOAD / TITLE	DESCRIPTION
		1P-20	Vanity Receptacle	GFCI Protected
		1P-15	Vanity Light, Ceiling Lighting	GFCI Protected if over tub or shower
		1P-15	Exhaust Fan and Light	GFCI Protected if over tub or shower
OPTIONS - Depending on Actual Layout:				
		1P-15	Exh. Fan, Light, Heat Combo	GFCI Protected if over tub or shower
		2P-20	Floor Heat System	GFCI Protected
		1P-15	Towel Warmer	GFCI Protected
		1P-20	Jacuzzi Whirlpool Tub	GFCI Protected
Shared GFCI Circuit			Receptacle/Plug Strip	In Vanity for Charging Devices
Shared GFCI Circuit			Receptacle/Fixture Box	Lighted Make Up Mirror

Notes: A dedicated 20 amp GFCI Receptacle circuit may be used for up to five bathrooms.
One GFCI Protected receptacle is required for each sink. Telephone or Intercom service is optional.

Bathroom Electrical Code Basics

	Bathroom lighting must be either: on dimmer switches, provide a "manual-on occupancy sensor", or be all fluorescent lighting.
	Bathroom receptacles are to be supplied by at least one 20 amp branch circuit. This circuit shall have no other outlets except bathroom receptacles. Bathroom outlets must be protected by a GFCI device.
	All bathroom exhaust fans shall provide a minimum of 5 air changes per hour.
	Hydro massage bathtubs and their associated electrical components must have GFCI - ground fault circuit interrupter. All electric motors shall be readily accessible for servicing purposes.

Electrical Codes for Bathroom GFCI

✓	Location(s)	Category	Device(s)	Description
☐	bathrooms	GFCI	vent fans exhaust fans	Vent fans installed directly above showers must be GFCI protected per manufacturer's instructions.
☐	hydromassage bathtubs Jacuzzi	GFCI	vent fans exhaust fans	Vent fans installed directly above showers must be GFCI protected per manufacturer's instructions.
☐	bathroom	wiring	GFCI receptacles	All receptacles must be GFCI protected on a 20 amp circuit, and at least one must be installed within 3 feet of each sink. GFCI devices must be installed in a readily accessible location.
☐	rooms	heating cables	GFCI	GFCI protection for personnel shall be provided for cables installed in electrically heated floors of rooms, kitchens, and in hydromassage bathtub locations.
☐	hydromassage bathtubs Jacuzzi	GFCI		Hydro-massage bathtub electrical equipment must be GFCI protected and should be on a dedicated 20 amp circuit.
☐	hydromassage bathtubs Jacuzzi	circuit	20 amp circuit	Hydro-massage bathtub electrical equipment must be GFCI protected and should be on a dedicated 20 amp circuit.

Living Room Entry Wiring Plan

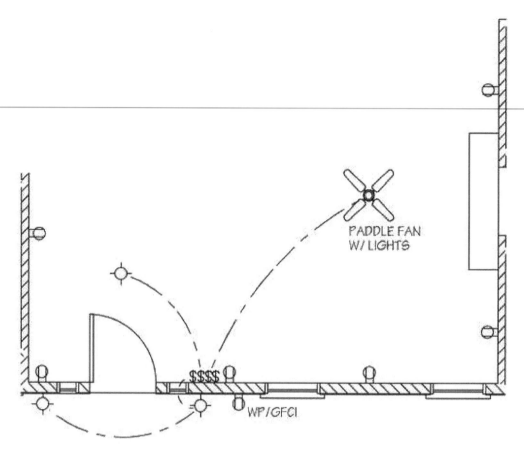

LIVING ROOM				
CKT#	LOAD	BRKR	LOAD / TITLE	DESCRIPTION
		1P-15	Wall Receptacles	AFCI Protected
		1P-15	Lighting, Ceiling Fan	Floor and Countertop
		1P-15	Ceiling Fan	Floor and Countertop
		1P-20	Porch Receptacle	GFCI Protected
OPTIONS - Depending on Actual Layout:				
shared on circuit			Receptacle and Switch	Gas Fireplace Insert
Notes:				

Electrical Codes for Living Room Pg-1

✓	Location(s)	Category	Device(s)	Description
☐	dwelling unit family room, dining room, living room, parlors, libraries, dens, bedrooms, sunrooms, recreation rm, closets, hallways	wiring methods	AFCI outlet circuit, individual branch circuit	It is permitted to have protection at the first outlet if the wiring method between the circuit breaker and the outlet is RMC, IMC, EMT, MC, or steel-armored cable (type AC) and if metal junction or outlet boxes are used.
☐	dwelling unit family room, dining room, living room, parlors, libraries, dens, bedrooms, sunrooms, recreation rm, closets, hallways	wiring methods	AFCI outlet circuit, individual branch circuit	All 120 volt 15 and 20 amp branch circuits where the branch circuit is EMT, PVC, ENT, or other listed metal or nonmetallic conduit or tubing which is installed in not less than 2 inches of concrete for the portion of the branch circuit between the branch circuit over current device and the first outlet shall be protected by a listed arc-fault circuit interrupter at the first outlet.
☐	dwelling unit family room, dining room, living room, parlors, libraries, dens, bedrooms, sunrooms, recreation rm, closets, hallways	wiring methods	AFCI outlet circuit, individual branch circuit	All 120 volt 15 and 20 amp branch circuits supplying outlets in the required areas shall be protected by a listed AFCI arc-fault circuit interrupter, combination-type, installed to provide protection of the branch circuit.

Electrical Codes for Living Room Pg-2

✓	Location(s)	Category	Device(s)	Description
☐	dwelling unit family rooms, dining rooms, living rooms, parlors, libraries, dens, bedrooms, sunrooms, recreation rooms, closets, hallways	wiring methods	AFCI	Where the branch circuit wiring has been modified, replaced, or extended, the branch circuit shall be protected by a listed combination-type AFCI that is located at the origin of the branch circuit, or a listed outlet branch-circuit type AFCI located at the first receptacle outlet of the existing branch circuit.
☐	living room	wiring	receptacles	Receptacle outlets must be spaced so that no point along the wall is farther than 6 feet from the nearest outlet. A fireplace, doorway or similar opening is not required to be counted as wall space. Receptacles must be located within 6 feet of each side of these spaces.
☐	living room	wiring methods	receptacles	Fixed panels such as the portion of a sliding glass door that is not movable must be considered wall space.
☐	living room	wiring methods	receptacles	Space occupied by a countertop must be counted as wall space and satisfied the requirement for placing receptacles along the wall. No point along the wall can be further than 6 feet from a receptacle.
☐	living room	wiring methods	receptacles	Wall space 2 feet or greater must have a receptacle outlet.

Electrical Codes for Living Room Pg-3

✓	Location(s)	Category	Device(s)	Description
☐	living room	wiring methods	receptacles	If a wall space is not available, receptacles must be installed on the floor. Receptacles installed on the floor must be within 18 inches of the wall to be counted as a required receptacle. Floor boxes and covers must be listed for floor use.
☐	living room	wiring methods	light outlet-switched plug	A switched light outlet is required. Lighting fixture or switched plug is acceptable.
☐	living room	wiring methods	wetbar track lighting GFCI, GFCI receptacles	GFCI protection is required for all 120-volt, 15 or 20-amp receptacles located within 6 feet of a wet bar sink. No exceptions for single outlet or dedicated appliances. GFCI devices must be installed in a readily accessible location.
☐	living room	installing	tamper resistant receptacles	All 125-volt, 15- and 20- amp receptacles installed in dwelling units shall be listed tamper-resistant.
☐	bonus room living room	lighting	track lighting	Track lighting is not allowed less than 5 feet above the floor unless protected from damage.
☐	bedroom living room family room living-area	wiring methods and common cable type	lights and receptacles circuit wiring	14/2 with ground NM Copper, 15 Amp Breaker
☐	laundry room bedroom living room family room living-area	wiring methods and common cable type	lights and receptacles circuit wiring	12/2 with ground NM Copper, 20 Amp Breaker

Home·Electrical·Wiring

Laundry Wiring Plan

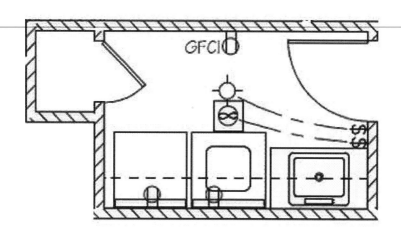

CKT#	LOAD	BRKR	LOAD / TITLE	VOLTS / DESCRIPTION
LAUNDRY ROOM				
		2P-30	Dryer	240V Receptacle
		1P-20	Washer	120V GFCI Receptacle
		1P-15	Light & Exhaust Fan	120V
OPTIONS - Depending on Actual Layout:				
		1P-20	Ironing Board Receptacles	GFCI Protected
		1P-20	Dryer Closet	Single Outlet Receptacle

Notes:
Telephone or Intercom service.

Electrical Codes for Laundry Pg-1

✓	Location(s)	Category	Device(s)	Description
☐	laundry room	wiring methods	receptacles	A dedicated 20 amp circuit is required for laundry receptacle outlets. No other devices are allowed on the laundry receptacle circuit, such as lights or receptacles located in another room.
☐	laundry room	wiring methods	receptacles	At least 1 receptacle outlet of a 20 amp circuit is required in every dwelling unit for laundry purposes.
☐	laundry room	wiring methods	lighting	At least one wall switch controlled lighting fixture is required.
☐	laundry room	wiring	GFCI receptacle outlet	GFCI protection is required for all 120 volt 15 or 20 amp receptacles located within 6 feet of a utility sink. No exceptions for single outlet or dedicated appliances. GFCI devices must be installed in a readily accessible location.
☐	laundry room	branch circuits and outlets	receptacles	A 30 amp circuit is the minimum requirement for an electric dryer which is wired with 10 AWG Cu, or 8 AWG AL.
☐	laundry room	branch circuits and outlets	receptacles	In an existing laundry room a 3-wire circuit is allowed to remain in use.
☐	laundry room	circuit 4-wire	outlet receptacle	4-wire 30 amp circuit is required for electric dryers.
☐	laundry room	branch circuits and outlets	receptacles	An electric dryer requires a 4-conductor branch circuit.
☐	laundry room	receptacles	tamper resistant	All 15 and 20 amp 120 volt receptacle outlets in dwelling units shall be listed tamper-resistant.

Electrical Codes for Laundry Pg-2

✓	Location(s)	Category	Device(s)	Description
☐	laundry room	wiring methods common cable types	receptacles	20 Amp Breaker- 12/2 with ground NM Copper
☐	laundry room	wiring methods common cable types	switches	20 Amp Breaker- 12/2 with ground NM Copper
☐	laundry	wiring methods common cable types	dryer-clothes	30 Amp Breaker- 10/3 with ground NM Copper
☐	laundry room bedroom living room family room living-area	wiring methods common cable type	lights and receptacles circuit wiring	12/2 with ground NM Copper
☐	laundry room bedroom living room family room living-area panel circuit	wiring methods common cable types	lights and receptacles circuit breaker	20 Amp Breaker

Garage Wiring Plan

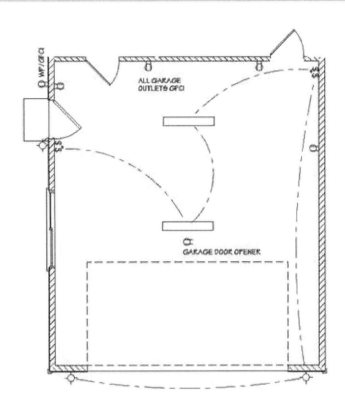

GARAGE CIRCUITS				
CKT#	**LOAD**	**BRKR**	**LOAD / TITLE**	**DESCRIPTION**
		1P-20	Wall Receptacles	GFCI Protected
		1P-15	Lighting	Garage, Driveway, Side Entry
OPTIONS - Depending on Actual Layout:				
		2P-60	Sub-Panel	240V Work Area and Equipment
		2P-30	Water Heater	240V
		1P-20	Vacuum System	Central Vacuum System
		1P-20	Washer	Clothes Washer
		2P-30	Dryer	Clothes Dryer
		1P-20	Furnace	Central Furnace

Notes: Garage door opener does not need GFCI Protection if it is a single outlet.
Lighting may be shared with another lighting circuit depending on circuit load.

Electrical Codes for Garage and Workshop Pg-1

✔	Location(s)	Category	Device(s)	Description
P1-The Main Electrical Service:				
☐	detached buildings garages outbuildings			The garage may have snap switches or 3-way switches.
☐	detached buildings	panels		Feeder conductors and overcurrent protection to detached garages must be based on the calculated load.
P2-Rough-In Wiring Methods:				
☐	rooms, kitchen	wiring methods	countertop receptacles	Receptacle outlets shall be located on, or above, but not more than 20 inches above the countertop. Receptacle outlet assemblies listed for the application shall be permitted to be installed in countertops. Receptacle outlets rendered not readily accessible by appliances fastened in place, appliance garages, sinks, or range tops, or appliances occupying dedicated space shall not be considered as these required outlets.
☐	basement, attached garage, accessory buildings	wiring methods	receptacles	At least one receptacle outlet, in addition to those for specific equipment, shall be installed in each basement, in each attached garage, or accessory building with electric power.
☐	detached buildings	wiring methods	receptacles, lighting	Receptacle and lighting requirements are the same for attached and detached garages.
☐	garage	wiring methods	receptacles	At least one receptacle outlet is required in attached garages. This requirement also applies to detached garages with electric power.

Electrical Codes for Garage and Workshop Pg-2

✓	Location(s)	Category	Device(s)	Description
☐		lighting outlets		Min. 1 wall-switched lighting outlet in garage.
☐		lighting outlets		Lighting outlet not required at garage vehicle doors.
☐		lighting outlets		Lighting outlet required at garage egress doors.
☐	detached buildings	wiring methods	receptacles, lighting	Receptacle and lighting requirements are the same for attached and detached garages.
☐	garage	wiring methods	lighting	Switched lighting fixture is required on the exterior to illuminate all personnel entrances. Light fixture is not required for vehicle doors such as overhead garage doors.
☐	garage	wiring methods	lighting	Wall switch controlled lighting outlet is required.
☐	outside	wiring methods	lighting outside	Switched lighting fixture is required on the exterior to illuminate all personnel entrances. Light fixture is not required for vehicle doors such as overhead garage doors.
☐	unfinished basement	wiring methods	lighting	A switched lighting fixture is required on the exterior to illuminate all personnel entrances. Light fixture is not required for vehicle doors such as overhead garage doors.

✓	Location(s)	Category	Device(s)	Description
☐	garage	wiring	GFCI receptacles	GFCI protection is required for all 15 and 20 amp 120 volt receptacles in the garage. GFCI devices must be installed in a readily accessible location.
☐	garage	wiring	GFCI receptacles	All 15 and 20 amp 120 volt receptacles within 6 feet of a utility sink must be GFCI protected. GFCI devices must be installed in a readily accessible location.
☐	detached buildings	wiring methods	grounding	Where the detached garage is served by only one branch circuit a grounding electrode system is not required. (1-20 amp 120 volt circuit installed for lighting and general use receptacles would not require a ground rod or connection to metal piping.)
☐	detached buildings	panels		Where there are metallic paths from the building supplying the detached garage, 4 wires must be run to the panel.
☐	detached buildings	panels		Where there are no metallic paths from the building supplying the detached garage, 3 wires may be run to the panel. (Install bonding jumper between the neutral and ground bar and connect the grounding electrode conductor to the grounding bar. Metallic paths include metal conduit, metal water piping, etc.)
☐		appliances	carbon monoxide alarms	Required in outside sleeping areas in dwellings with fuel-fired appliances or with attached garages
☐	garage	wiring methods common cable types	water heater-30 amp	30 Amp Breaker- 10/2 with ground NM Copper

Electrical Codes for Garage and Workshop Pg-4

✓	Location(s)	Category	Device(s)	Description
P4-Install the Device:				
☐	garage	receptacles	tamper resistant	All 125-volt, 15- and 20- amp receptacles installed in dwelling units shall be listed tamper-resistant.
☐	garage	wiring	receptacles GFCI exception #1	GFCI protection is not required if receptacles are not readily accessible. This applies to ceiling receptacles for the garage door opener. GFCI devices must be installed in a readily accessible location.
☐	garage	wiring	receptacles GFCI exception #2	GFCI protection is not required for receptacles within dedicated space for appliances that are not easily moved. This applies to single receptacles for a refrigerator or vacuum system, a duplex receptacle for a refrigerator and a freezer. GFCI devices must be installed in a readily accessible location.
☐	garage	wiring methods common cable types	water heater- 30 amp	30 Amp Breaker- 10/2 with ground NM Copper

Unfinished Basement Wiring Plan

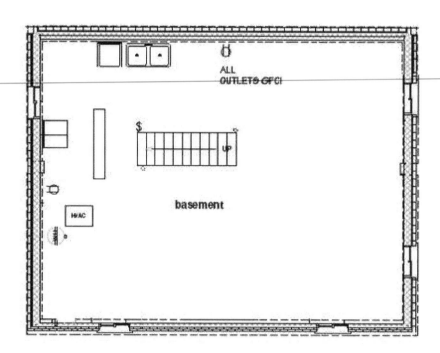

ALL
OUTLETS GFCI

basement

HVAC

BASEMENT CIRCUITS				
CKT#	LOAD	BRKR	LOAD / TITLE	DESCRIPTION
		1P-20	Wall Receptacles	GFCI Protected
		1P-15	Lighting	General Area
OPTIONS - Depending on Actual Layout:				
		2P-30	Water Heater	240V
		1P-20	Washer	Clothes Washer
		2P-30	Dryer	Clothes Dryer
		1P-20	Furnace	Central Furnace
Notes: GFCI Protection is required in an unfinished basement. Lighting may be shared with another lighting circuit depending on circuit load.				

Electrical Codes for Basement Pg-1

✓	Location(s)	Category	Device(s)	Description
☐	basement, attached garage, accessory buildings	wiring methods	receptacles	At least one receptacle outlet, in addition to those for specific equipment, shall be installed in each basement, in each attached garage, or accessory building with electric power.
☐	unfinished basement	wiring methods	receptacles	Where a portion of the basement is finished into a habitable room, at least one receptacle outlet is required in each unfinished portion.
☐	unfinished basement	wiring methods	lighting	A switched lighting fixture is required on the exterior to illuminate all personnel entrances. Light fixture is not required for vehicle doors such as overhead garage doors.
☐	unfinished basement	wiring methods	lighting	A wall switch controlled lighting outlet is required.
☐	unfinished basement	wiring	GFCI receptacles exception #3	GFCI protection is not required for receptacle supplying a permanently installed burglar or fire alarm system. GFCI devices must be installed in a readily accessible location.
☐	unfinished basement	wiring	GFCI receptacles - washer refrigerator freezer	GFCI protection is not required for receptacles within dedicated space for appliances that are not easily moved. This applies to single receptacles for a washer, or a duplex receptacle for a refrigerator and a freezer.
☐	unfinished basement	wiring	accessible GFCI receptacles	GFCI protection is not required if receptacles are not readily accessible. GFCI devices must be installed in a readily accessible location.

Electrical Codes for Basement Pg-2

✓	Location(s)	Category	Device(s)	Description
☐	basement	receptacles	receptacles	All 15 and 20 amp 120 volt receptacles within 6 feet of a utility sink must be GFCI protected, even if installed for dedicated appliances.
☐	rooms	wiring methods	smoke detector	Smoke detectors must be located on each level of the dwelling unit including basements, but NOT crawl spaces or uninhabitable attics.
☐	home	smoke alarms	smoke alarms	Smoke alarm systems are required for each story including basements and habitable attics.
☐	unfinished basement	wiring		Cables containing wires smaller than two #6 or three #8 are not allowed to be secured directly to ceiling joists. These cables must be routed through bored holes or installed on running boards.
☐	unfinished basement	wiring	cable	NM cable used on the wall of an unfinished basement is permitted to be installed in listed conduit. NM cable installed in conduit must be a have a non-metallic bushing installed at the point where the cable enters the conduit.
☐	unfinished basement	wiring	cable	NM cable must closely follow the surface of the building or be protected from damage. Horizontal runs of exposed cable must be protected.
☐	unfinished basement	receptacles	tamper resistant	All 125 volt, 15 and 20 amp receptacles installed in dwelling units shall be listed tamper-resistant.

Home Electrical Circuits

CIRCUITS

120 VOLT CIRCUITS

Home·Electrical·Wiring

240 VOLT CIRCUITS

Home·Electrical·Wiring

EXTERIOR CIRCUITS

Home Electrical Circuits

BEDROOM AFCI	15 AMP 120 VOLT	BEDROOM AFCI
W-HOUSE FAN	15 AMP 120 VOLT	WHOLE HOUSE FAN
SMK-DETS LTS	15 AMP 120 VOLT	SMOKE DETS / LIGHTS
LVG ROOM	15 AMP 120 VOLT	LIVING RM LIGHTS / PLUGS
REFER	15 AMP 120 VOLT	REFRIGERATOR
KITCHEN GFCI	20 AMP 120 VOLT	KITCHEN GFCI OUTLETS
KITCHEN GFCI	20 AMP 120 VOLT	KITCHEN GFCI OUTLETS
DISHWASHER DISPOSAL	20 AMP 120 VOLT	DISPOSAL DISHWASHER
BATH GFCI	20 AMP 120 VOLT	BATHROOM GFCI
FURNACE	20 AMP 120 VOLT	FURNACE
DRYER	30 AMP 240 VOLT	DRYER
DRYER	30 AMP 240 VOLT	DRYER
RANGE	50 AMP 240 VOLT	RANGE
RANGE	50 AMP 240 VOLT	RANGE
SERVICE DISCONNECT	100 AMP 240 VOLT	MAIN BREAKER
WASHER	20 AMP 120 VOLT	WASHER
GARAGE GFCI	20 AMP 120 VOLT	GARAGE GFCI

Electrical Circuit Schedule

Panel Size: _____ Amps, Make: _____ Model: _____

CKT#	LOAD	BRKR	LOAD / TITLE	DESCRIPTION

Minimum Electrical Service Load Calculator

STEP	Circuit Load Description	Calculation / watts	Watts
	Total Square Footage of the Home: _____ Sq. Ft.		
1	**Lighting and General Purpose Receptacles**	3 watts X Total Sq .Ft.	
2	**Small Appliances:**		
	Two in the Kitchen	1,500 watts each X 2	3,000
	One in the Laundry	1,500 watts each X 1	1,500
3	**Large Appliances & Equipment:**		
	Range / Oven	8,000 watts	
	Dishwasher & Garbage Disposal	2,000 watts	
	Clothes Dryer	4500 watts	
	Water Heater	4500 watts	
4	**HVAC - Heating and Air Conditioning:**	List the one highest watt equipment only:	
	Furnace		
	Air Conditioning		
	Heat Pump		
5		**TOTAL WATTS:**	
6		**Factor 100% of the first 10,000 watts**	10,000
7		**Balance after subtracting 10,000 watts (Step 5 - 10,000)**	
8		**Calculate 40% of the Balance watts shown in Step 7 (_____ watts X .40)**	
	Estimate the Electrical Load:		
9		**Add Step 6 (10,000) + Step 8**	
	Convert to Amperage:		
10		**Determine the Amperage by Calculating Step 9 X 240 volts**	

Electrical Circuit Planner: Worksheet

ELECTRICAL SERVICE LOAD PLANNER			
LOAD DESCRIPTION	AMPS	VOLTS	WATTS
	Note: Amps X Volts = Watts		

120 Volt Receptacles

Wiring a 120 Volt Grounded Receptacle Outlet

A 120 volt grounded receptacle outlet is supplied with three wires, Black Power, White Neutral and Green or Bare Ground. The attachment terminations may be made to screws or quick-connections, depending on the brand receptacle which is selected.

The face or front and back of a 15 Amp 120 Volt grounded receptacle.
The right power side has a smaller opening. Wiring the 15 Amp 120 Volt Receptacle:
Brass is for Power, Silver is for the Neutral, Green is for Ground.

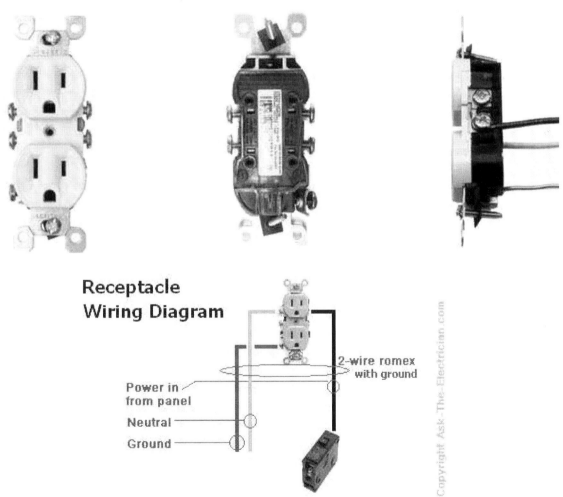

Wiring Note: A 15 amp rated receptacle may be installed on a 20 amp circuit, but a 20 amp rated receptacle may not be installed on a 15 amp circuit.

Home·Electrical·Wiring

Circuit Design: 20 Amp 120 Volt Outlet

Example of a 20 Amp 120 Volt Circuit:

A 20 amp receptacle outlet circuit will be found in the kitchen for the dishwasher and garbage disposal.

Circuit Design Table: 20 Amp 120 Volt		
Device: **20 Amp Receptacle**	**Outlet Symbol**	**Applications:** **Garage, Bathroom, Kitchen**
Circuit Size: **20 Amps, 120 Volt**	**Cable: Romex** **12/2 with Ground**	**Box / Enclosure:** **1-Gang, Side Nail**

Circuit Notes:

A 20 amp 120 volt circuit is commonly installed for equipment such as:

Kitchen Microwave Oven, Dishwasher and Disposal, Heater or Furnace, and other devices installed in areas where GFCI protection is not required.

Circuit Design: 120 Volt GFCI Receptacle Outdoor

Example of a 120 Volt GFCI:

An exterior outlet must be located at the front and rear entrances to the home providing GFCI protection and a weatherproof cover.

Circuit Design Table: 120 Volt GFCI		
Device: GFCI Receptacle	**GFCI Outlet Symbol**	**Applications:** Front and Rear Entrances
	GFCI	
Circuit Size: 20 Amps, 120 Volt	**Cable:** #12 THWN	**Box / Enclosure:** 1-Gang, Weather Proof Box

Wiring Notes:

When the electrical wiring is being installed in the home the outside finished siding may not be in place so a length of the circuit cable should be installed and fastened inside the framed wall just inside of where the outside receptacle will be located. The cable should be secured so that it will not be damaged by insulation or sheet rock, but is must also be available so that if a cut in box is installed then you will be able to retrieve the cable and complete the installation.

Wiring GFCI Receptacles

GFCI Receptacles and how they are wired to provide protection to one or multiple devices and locations of the same circuit.

Options and Methods for Wiring GFCI Receptacles

Wiring a Single GFCI Receptacle

- The basics of wiring a single GFCI outlet.

GFCI Wiring the Feed Through Method

- Wiring a GFCI receptacle using the feed through method which will protect more than one receptacle outlet on the same circuit.

Tailed Wiring Method

- Wiring a GFCI using the tailed method enables you to install one GFCI outlet to protect one location without affecting other devices that share the same circuit.

GFCI: Wiring a Single Receptacle

In this example the GFCI protection serves this outlet location only.

Notice that this GFCI Outlet comes with yellow tape over the LOAD side.

The wire leading to this location may be an extension from another branch circuit or it could be a single circuit being served from a panel or sub-panel.

When wiring a GFCI outlet you will be attaching the wiring to the LINE area of the receptacle.

Wiring a single GFCI outlet for the protection for one outlet location. This method will provide GFCI protection to the immediate location only.

GFCI: Feed Through Wiring for Receptacles

GFCI receptacle wiring to protect multiple receptacles.

Identify the cable to be used for the LINE feed.
Identify the cable to be used for the LOAD feed.

Remove the yellow warning sticker to expose the LOAD area and terminals.

Identify the LINE area of the GFCI Receptacle.

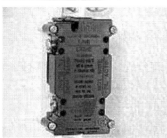

First attach the LINE black wire to the LINE hot wire terminal, and the LINE white wire to the LINE white wire terminal.

Next attach the LOAD black wire to the LOAD hot wire terminal, and the LOAD white wire to the LOAD white wire terminal.

Wiring a GFCI receptacle to protect multiple locations. This method will provide GFCI protection to multiple locations.

Home·Electrical·Wiring

GFCI: Pig Tail Wiring

How to wire a GFCI receptacle to be protected independently of the other devices on the same circuit.

With the circuit power OFF, prepare the circuit wires to be spliced together with the pig-tailed wires.

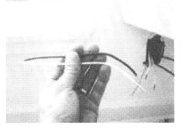

Measure out two "pig-tails" or lengths of wire about 6 to 8 inches long, one black and white insulated wire.

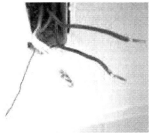

Twist the wires together evenly; trim the ends of the wires so they are even, then screw the wire connector firmly.

Fold the spliced wires back into the back of the box making room for the GFCI receptacle.
Next attach the ground wire to the provided ground screw connection.
Attach the tails to the LINE side of the GFCI receptacle - black to the hot wire terminal, and the white to the white wire terminal.

Notice that the yellow label is covering the LOAD side of the GFCI receptacle which is not used.
Install the GFCI receptacle and mount the cover plate.
This GFCI receptacle will now operate independently from the rest of the circuit devices.

Circuit Design: 20 Amp 120 Volt Circuit

Example of a 20 Amp 120 Volt Circuit:
A 20 Amp GFCI Circuit will be found in the garage, bathroom and kitchen.

Circuit Design Table: 120 Volt 20 Amp Circuit		
Device: 20 Amp Receptacle	**Outlet Symbol**	**Applications:** Garage, Bathroom, Kitchen
	GFCI	
Circuit Size: 20 Amps, 120 Volt	**Cable: Type NM** 12/2 with Ground	**Box / Enclosure:** 1-Gang, Side Nail

Circuit Notes:
GFCI protection is required for the receptacle outlets in the garage, bathroom, kitchen, and in outside locations. The GFCI protection may be provided by installing a GFCI circuit breaker which will protect all the devices connected to the circuit.

Bathroom GFCI Circuit Wiring

Wiring a Bathroom GFCI Circuit

Shown below are two wiring methods typically used when wiring multiple bathrooms.

One GFCI for each Bathroom   **One GFCI for all Bathrooms**

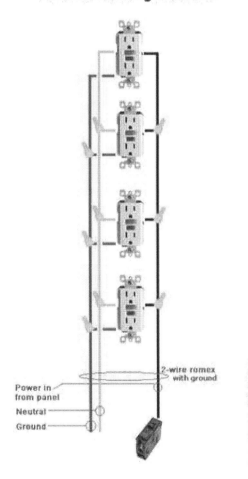

Bathroom GFCI Circuit
Parallel Wiring Method

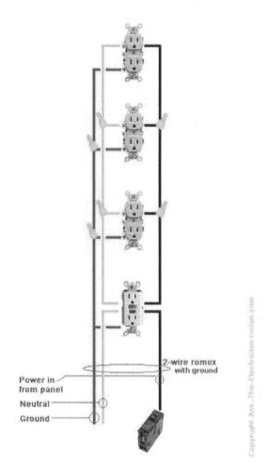

Bathroom GFCI Circuit
One Master GFCI Wiring Method

When this wiring method is used each bathroom is protected by its own GFCI receptacle and if any GFCI trips OFF it will not affect the other GFCI receptacles on the same circuit.

When this method is used, if the master GFCI trips OFF then all of the remaining receptacles on the same circuit will trip OFF as well.

Wiring Note: Up to five bathrooms may be on the same circuit, however if the anticipated connected load will be high then additional circuits should be considered.

Electrical Codes for Bathrooms Pg-1

✓	Location(s)	Category	Device(s)	Description
☐	bathroom	definition	bathroom	An area including a bathroom with one or more of the following: a toilet, a urinal, a tub, a shower, a bidet, or similar plumbing fixtures.
☐	bathrooms	GFCI	vent fans exhaust fans	Vent fans installed directly above showers must be GFCI protected per manufacturer's instructions.
☐	bathroom	20 amp circuit		A dedicated 20 amp circuit is required in bathrooms for receptacles.
☐	bathroom	20 amp circuit		A separate 20 amp circuit is required for bathroom receptacles only.
☐	bathroom	20 amp circuit		Different bathroom receptacles only may be served from one 20 amp circuit.
☐	bathroom	20 amp circuit		No other device allowed on the receptacle circuit unless the dedicated 20 amp circuit supplies only one bathroom, such as lights, vent fans etc.
☐	bathroom	wiring methods	receptacles	At least 1 receptacle outlet shall be installed in bathrooms within 3 feet of the outside edge of each basin. The receptacle outlet shall be located on a wall or partition that is adjacent to the basin or basin countertop, located on the countertop, or installed on the side or face of the basin cabinet not more than 12 inches below the countertop. Receptacle outlet assemblies listed for the application shall be installed in the countertop.

Electrical Codes for Bathrooms Pg-2

✓	Location(s)	Category	Device(s)	Description
☐	bathroom	wiring	GFCI receptacles	All receptacles must be GFCI protected on a 20 amp circuit, and at least one must be installed within 3 feet of each sink. GFCI devices must be installed in a readily accessible location.
☐	bathroom	branch circuits	receptacles	Outlets may not be mounted face-up on a vanity countertop.
☐	bathroom	branch circuits	receptacles	No receptacles are allowed within or directly over a tub or shower.
☐	bathroom	wiring methods common cable types	GFI receptacles	20 Amp Breaker- 12/2 with ground NM Copper

Kitchen GFCI Circuit Wiring

Kitchen Appliance Circuits GFCI Protected

The two required appliance circuits are GFCI protected because they are typically located on counter top to the right and left sides of the kitchen sink.

Kitchen Appliance Circuit #1
One Master GFCI Wiring Method

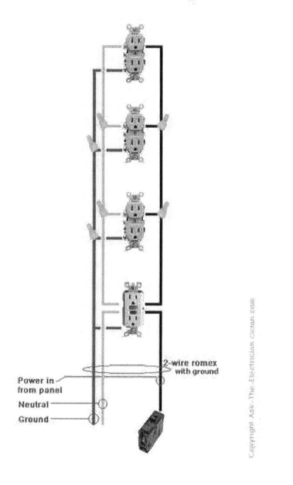

Kitchen Appliance Circuit #2
One Master GFCI Wiring Method

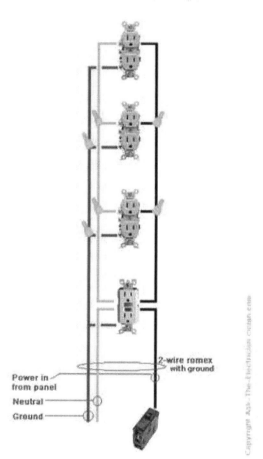

Due to the high electrical load demands for many kitchen appliances, there may be fewer receptacles for each appliance circuit which will help to prevent overloaded circuits.

Wiring Note: Additional circuits may be required depending on the size of the kitchen and the electrical circuit requirements for additional equipment or devices.

Home·Electrical·Wiring

Electrical Codes for Kitchens Pg-1

✓	Location(s)	Category	Device(s)	Description
☐	kitchen	wiring methods	receptacles	All receptacles in kitchen area must be on a 20 amp circuit.
☐	kitchen	wiring methods	AFCI outlet circuit	AFCI protected receptacles are not required in kitchens
☐	kitchens, pantries, breakfast room, dining room	wiring methods	countertop receptacles	Receptacles installed for countertop surfaces shall not be considered as the required receptacles for the room area.
☐	kitchen	wiring methods	receptacles	No point along the wall may be further than 6 feet from a receptacle, if not counter space.
☐	kitchen	wiring methods	circuits	No other device allowed on the receptacle circuits, such as lights or appliances. Receptacle for the refrigerator is allowed on the small appliance circuits or may be supplied from a dedicated 15 or 20 amp circuit.
☐	kitchen	branch circuits		A switched receptacle for a dining room light is permitted on a non small appliance circuit.
☐	kitchen	branch circuits		Small appliance circuits must serve the refrigerator and all countertop and exposed wall receptacles in the kitchen, dining room, and pantry.
☐	kitchen	wiring methods	circuits	Minimum of two 20 amp circuits required to supply kitchen counter top receptacles.

Electrical Codes for Kitchens Pg-2

✓	Location(s)	Category	Device(s)	Description
☐	kitchen cooktop	wiring methods	receptacles	If spacing behind the cooktop is 18 inches or greater, this area must be counted as wall space and receptacles must be installed so that no point along the countertop is further than 2 feet from a receptacle (or 1 receptacle every 4 feet).
☐	kitchen	counter	receptacles	Counter spaces longer than 1 foot require a receptacle.
☐	kitchen	kitchen receptacles	receptacles	Receptacles must be located so that no point along the countertop is further than 2 feet from a receptacle (or 1 receptacle every 4 feet).
☐	kitchen island	wiring methods	receptacles	An island requires a receptacle only if larger than 24 inches by 12 inches. If a sink or cooktop is installed on the island and the width of the counter behind the appliance is less than 12 inches a receptacle must be installed on both sides. (Locate receptacle no more than 12 inches below cabinet.)
☐	kitchen peninsula	wiring methods	receptacles	A peninsula requires a receptacle only if larger than 24 inches by 12 inches. If a sink or cooktop is installed on the island and the width of the counter behind the appliance is less than 12 inches a receptacle must be installed on both sides. (Locate receptacle no more than 12 inches below cabinet.)

Electrical Codes for Kitchens Pg-3

✓	Location(s)	Category	Device(s)	Description
☐	kitchen		receptacles	Island and peninsula countertop spaces require 1 receptacle per space. The 24 inch rule does not apply.
☐	kitchen cooktop	wiring methods	receptacles	If spacing behind the cooktop is less than 18 inches one receptacle is required within 2 feet of each side of the cooktop.
☐	kitchen sink	wiring methods	receptacles	If spacing behind the sink is less than 12 inches, one plug is required within 2 feet of each side of the sink.
☐	kitchen	wiring methods	receptacles	Island and peninsula receptacles are permitted 12 inches or less below a counter overhanging and where there is no means of installing a receptacle in an overhead cabinet.
☐	rooms, kitchen	wiring methods	receptacles	Receptacles typically 48 inches above floor to top of box, no more than 20 inches above the countertop to count as a required outlet
☐	kitchen		receptacles	Receptacles are required on each wall that is 3 feet or less in foyers that are greater than 60 sq ft.
☐	kitchen		receptacles	Receptacles that are a part of electrical baseboard heaters may be used as the required outlets.
☐	kitchen		receptacles	Receptacles that are more than 5 1/2 feet high may not be used as the required outlets.

Electrical Codes for Kitchens Pg-4

✓	Location(s)	Category	Device(s)	Description
☐	kitchen	wiring methods	GFCI receptacles	Receptacles installed to serve countertop surfaces must be GFCI protected. GFCI devices must be installed in a readily accessible location.
☐	kitchen	receptacles	tamper resistant	All 125-volt, 15- and 20- amp receptacles installed in dwelling units shall be listed tamper-resistant.
☐	kitchen	wiring methods common cable types	receptacles	20 Amp Breaker- 12/2 with ground NM Copper

➤Home·Electrical·Wiring➤

Wiring Diagram: Switched Outlet - Disposal #1

Example: Kitchen Garbage Disposal

This switched outlet is commonly used in the kitchen for the garbage disposal where the circuit may be shared with the dishwasher.

The power source is located at the switch box.

This diagram shows the power entering into the circuit at the switch box location, then sending one power line for the dishwasher and a switched leg for the garbage disposal.

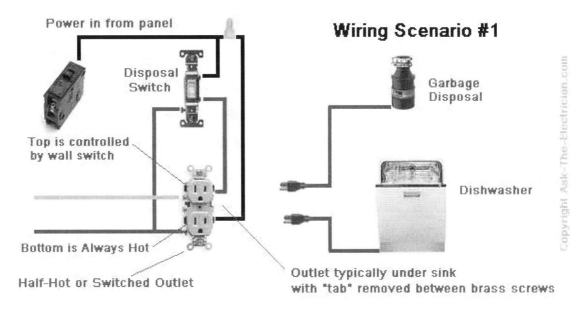

NOTE:
See the tab removal adjustment process for the receptacle outlet.

Wiring Diagram: Switched Disposal Outlet - #2

Example: Kitchen Garbage Disposal

This Switched outlet is commonly used in the kitchen for the garbage disposal where the circuit may be shared with the dishwasher.

The power source is located at the outlet box.

This diagram shows the power entering the circuit at the grounded outlet box location, and then sending power up to the switch and a switched leg back down to the outlet.

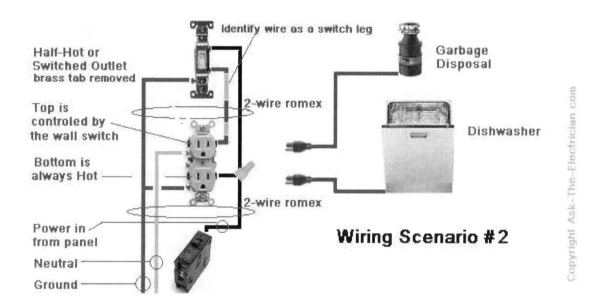

NOTE:
See the tab removal adjustment process for the receptacle outlet.

Electrical Codes for Kitchen Disposal

✓	Location(s)	Category	Device(s)	Description
☐	kitchen	dishwasher and disposal	receptacles	Flex cord must use 3 wire type, not shorter than 18 to 36 inches for disposal, may be hard wired.
☐	kitchen	dishwasher and disposal	receptacles	Receptacles must be located in the space occupied by the dishwasher or adjacent cabinet.
☐	kitchen	disposal	hardwired	If dishwasher is hardwired and not within sight of the circuit breaker then a lockout bracket must be installed.
☐	kitchen	disposal	receptacles	Switch is allowed for the disposal disconnect if not cord and plug connected.
☐	kitchen	wiring methods common cable types	dish washer/disposal	20 Amp Breaker- 12/2 with ground NM Copper

Wiring Diagram: Switched Receptacle Outlet #1

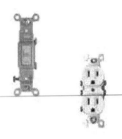

Example: Living Rooms and Bedrooms

This Switched outlet is commonly used to turn on floor lamps or night stand lights.

This setup is also known as Half Hot outlets.

The power source is located at the switch box.

The diagram shows the power entering into the circuit at the switch box location, then sending one power line for the outlet which is hot all the time and a switched leg for the top half of the outlet being used for a table lamp or a floor fixture.

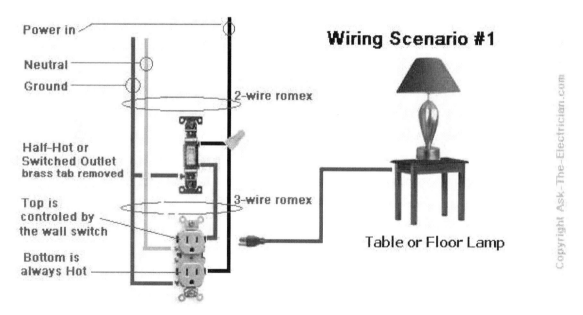

NOTE:
See the tab removal adjustment process for the receptacle outlet.

Wiring Diagram: Switched Receptacle Outlet #2

Example: Living Rooms and Bedrooms
This Switched outlet is commonly used to turn on floor lamps or night stand lights.
This setup is also known as Half Hot outlets.

The power source is located at the outlet box.

The diagram below shows the power entering the circuit at the grounded outlet box location, and then sending power up to the switch and a switched leg back down to the outlet.

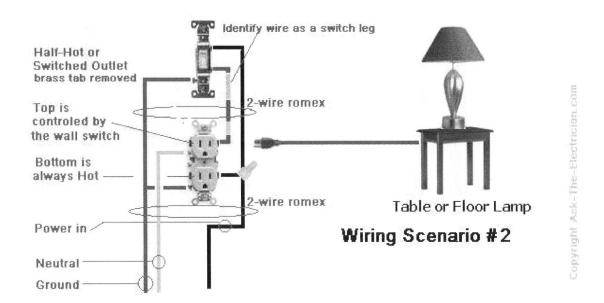

NOTE:
See the tab removal adjustment process for the receptacle outlet.

Switched Receptacle Outlet: Tab Removal

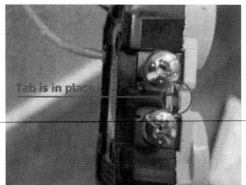

The Process for removing the tab link from the receptacle outlet.
This process applies to switched receptacle outlets found in rooms where used for floor lamps or table lamps, or in the kitchen where used for the garbage disposal.

Here is the bridge or tab that joins the upper and lower sections of the power side of the outlet together. This is a flat brass piece of metal.

By using a pair of needle nose pliers you can grip the flat tab of metal and with a side to side motion wiggle it back and forth until it breaks off. Side cutters are sometimes used but that can leave the metal in place or sticking out where it can become a problem.

Here the tab is removed and now the top and bottom outlets are separated from one another.

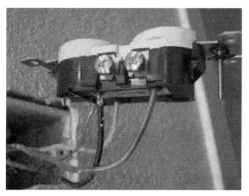

Notice the two separate colored wires, red for the light fixture which is controlled by the switch, and the black for the bottom outlet which is hot all the time. Notice that I have used the quick connect method because the lighting load is small. If the load was greater then I would have attached the wires to the screw terminals on the side.

Circuit Design: 15 Amp 120 Volt Lighting

Example of a 15 Amp 120 Volt Lighting Circuit:

A 15 amp circuit is commonly used for lighting in areas such as the kitchen, living room, and hallways.

Circuit Design Table: 120 Volt 15 Amp Outlet Circuit		
Device: **15 Amp Lighting**	**Lighting Symbol**	**Applications:** **Kitchen**
Circuit Size: **15 Amps, 120 Volt**	**Cable: Type NM** **14/2 with Ground**	**Box / Enclosure:** **Recessed Lighting Enclosure**

Circuit Notes:

A 15 amp 120 volt circuit is commonly installed for lighting such as: recessed lighting, surface mounted, and wall mounted light fixtures.

The total number of light fixtures that may be on the circuit will depend on the total watts, which is determined by adding up the number of lamps and watts for the total. The circuit should be loaded to 80%.

Electrical Codes for Lighting Pg-1

✓	Location(s)	Category	Device(s)	Description
☐	lighting fixture	wiring methods		White wire must be identified as hot with black tape or permanent marker at each termination point.
☐	bedrooms	wiring methods	AFCI outlet circuit	Arc Fault protection required for all outlets, defined by the NEC includes all lighting fixtures, smoke detectors, and receptacles.
☐	detached buildings	wiring methods	receptacles, lighting	Receptacle and lighting requirements are the same for attached and detached garages.
☐	room	wiring methods	lighting fixture	From panelboard or receptacle, power supply with 2-conductor with ground NM cable 120 volt.
☐	bathroom	wiring methods	lighting	At least one wall switch controlled lighting outlet is required.
☐	bonus room	wiring methods	light outlet-switched plug	A switched light outlet is required. Lighting fixture or switched plug is acceptable.
☐	kitchen	wiring methods	lighting	At least one wall switch controlled lighting fixture is required.
☐	laundry room	wiring methods	lighting	At least one wall switch controlled lighting fixture is required.
☐	living room	wiring methods	light outlet-switched plug	A switched light outlet is required. Lighting fixture or switched plug is acceptable.
☐	room occupied	wiring methods	light outlet-switched plug	A switched light outlet is required. Lighting fixture or switched plug is acceptable.

Electrical Codes for Lighting Pg-2

	Location(s)	Category	Device(s)	Description
☐	detached buildings	wiring methods	receptacles, lighting	Receptacle and lighting requirements are the same for attached and detached garages.
☐	garage	wiring methods	lighting	Switched lighting fixture is required on the exterior to illuminate all personnel entrances. Light fixture is not required for vehicle doors such as overhead garage doors.
☐	garage	wiring methods	lighting	Wall switch controlled lighting outlet is required.
☐	hallway	wiring methods	lighting	Wall switch controlled lighting outlet is required.
☐	outside	wiring methods	lighting outside	Switched lighting fixture is required on the exterior to illuminate all personnel entrances. Light fixture is not required for vehicle doors such as overhead garage doors.
☐	stairwell	wiring methods	lighting	Wall switch controlled lighting outlet is required.
☐	stairwell	wiring methods	lighting	Where there are 6 or more risers on the stairs, a wall switch to control the lighting outlet is required at each level. 3-way or 4-way switching is required.
☐	unfinished basement	wiring methods	lighting	A switched lighting fixture is required on the exterior to illuminate all personnel entrances. Light fixture is not required for vehicle doors such as overhead garage doors.

Electrical Codes for Lighting Pg-3

✓	Location(s)	Category	Device(s)	Description
☐	crawl space	wiring methods	lighting	Lighting outlet or fixture is required if space is used for storage or contains equipment that may need servicing. Light must be located at or near the equipment. This applies to equipment such as heating or air conditioning.
☐	crawl space	wiring methods	lighting	Switch for light outlet or fixture must be at the point of entrance to the space.
☐	inside equipment	wiring methods	lighting	Lighting outlet or fixture is required at or near the equipment.
☐	inside equipment	wiring methods	lighting	Switch for light outlet or fixture must be at the point of entrance to the space. A pull chain operated light fixture is allowed if located near the point of entry.
☐	unfinished basement	wiring methods	lighting	A wall switch controlled lighting outlet is required.
☐	living room	wiring methods	wetbar track lighting GFCI	GFCI protection is required for all 120 volt 15 or 20 amp receptacles located within 6 feet of a wet bar sink. No exceptions for single outlet or dedicated appliances. GFCI devices must be installed in a readily accessible location.
☐	detached buildings	wiring methods	grounding	Where the detached garage is served by only one branch circuit a grounding electrode system is not required. (1 20-amp 120-volt circuit installed for lighting and general use receptacles would not require a ground rod or connection to metal piping.)

Circuit Design: 15 Amp 120 Volt Outlet Circuit

Example of a 15 Amp 120 Volt Outlet Circuit:

A 15 amp receptacle outlet circuit will be found in areas not required to have AFCI protection or as adopted in each local area. These areas may include hallways, entry, den, entertainment room.

Circuit Design Table: 120 Volt 15 Amp Outlet Circuit		
Device: **15 Amp Receptacle**	**Outlet Symbol**	**Application:** **Living Room, Hallway,**
		FLOOR APPROVED OUTLET (verify location)
Circuit Size: **15 Amps, 120 Volt**	**Cable: Type NM** **14/2 with Ground**	**Box / Enclosure:** **1-Gang, Side Nail**

Circuit Notes:

A general purpose 15 amp 120 volt outlet circuit is commonly installed where AFCI protection is not required. The number of outlets may be 8 to 10; however special attention must be given to the area and devices that may be used. The 15 amp outlet circuit is not recommended in areas where high energy devices may be used, such as large flat screen televisions.

Electrical Codes for Receptacles Pg-1

✓	Location(s)	Category	Device(s)	Description
☐	in all areas	when wiring	switches or receptacles	A switch or receptacle that has wire conductors are to be wrapped clockwise under the binding screws to create full contact. This method is limited to #10 or smaller wire conductors.
☐	kitchen	wiring methods	receptacles	All receptacles in kitchen area must be on a 20 amp circuit.
☐	kitchen	wiring methods	receptacles	No point along the wall may be further than 6 feet from a receptacle, if not counter space.
☐	kitchen	wiring methods	circuits	Minimum of two 20 amp circuits required to supply kitchen counter top receptacles.
☐	kitchen cooktop	wiring methods	receptacles	If spacing behind the cooktop is 18 inches or greater, this area must be counted as wall space and receptacles must be installed so that no point along the countertop is further than 2 feet from a receptacle (or 1 receptacle every 4 feet)
☐	kitchen island	wiring methods	receptacles	An island requires a receptacle only if larger than 24 inches by 12 inches. If a sink or cooktop is installed on the island and the width of the counter behind the appliance is less than 12 inches a receptacle must be installed on both sides. (Locate receptacle no more than 12 inches below cabinet.)

Electrical Codes for Receptacles Pg-2

✓	Location(s)	Category	Device(s)	Description
☐	kitchen peninsula	wiring methods	receptacles	A peninsula requires a receptacle only if larger than 24 inches by 12 inches. If a sink or cooktop is installed on the island and the width of the counter behind the appliance is less than 12 inches a receptacle must be installed on both sides. (Locate receptacle no more than 12 inches below cabinet.)
☐	kitchen cooktop	wiring methods	receptacles	If spacing behind the cooktop is less than 18 inches one receptacle is required within 2 feet of each side of the cooktop.
☐	kitchen counters	wiring methods	receptacles	Counter spaces divided by range tops, refrigerators, or sinks must be considered separate spaces.
☐	kitchen sink	wiring methods	receptacles	If spacing behind the sink is less than 12 inches, one plug is required within 2 feet of each side of the sink.
☐	kitchen	wiring methods	receptacles	Island and peninsula receptacles are permitted 12 inches or less below a counter overhanging and where there is no means of installing a receptacle in an overhead cabinet.
☐	outside balconies, decks, porches	wiring methods	receptacles	Balconies, decks, and porches that are accessible from inside the dwelling unit shall have at least one receptacle outlet installed within the perimeter. The receptacle shall not be more than 6 1/2 feet above the surface.

Electrical Codes for Receptacles Pg-3

✓	Location(s)	Category	Device(s)	Description
☐	outside	wiring methods	receptacles	A receptacle outlet is required outdoors at the front and rear of every home. The receptacles should be not higher than 6 feet 6 inches.
☐	basement, attached garage, accessory buildings	wiring methods	receptacles	At least one receptacle outlet, in addition to those for specific equipment, shall be installed in each basement, in each attached garage, or accessory building with electric power.
☐	detached buildings	wiring methods	receptacles, lighting	Receptacle and lighting requirements are the same for attached and detached garages.
☐	garage	wiring methods	receptacles	At least one receptacle outlet is required in attached garages. This requirement also applies to detached garages with electric power.
☐	sheds, greenhouses, pool houses, pole barns	wiring methods	receptacles	At least one receptacle outlet, in addition to those for specific equipment, shall be installed in each shed, greenhouse, pool house, pole barn, with electric power.
☐	unfinished basement	wiring methods	receptacles	At least one receptacle outlet is required in unfinished basements.
☐	hallway	wiring methods	receptacles	Hallways 10 feet or more in length must have a receptacle outlet.
☐	foyers	wiring methods	receptacles	Foyers that are not part of a hallway that have an area that is greater than 60 square feet shall have a receptacle(s) located at each wall space 3 feet or more in width and unbroken by doorways, floor-to-ceiling windows, and similar openings.

Electrical Codes for Receptacles Pg-4

✓	Location(s)	Category	Device(s)	Description
☐	crawl space	wiring methods		Receptacles are required if heating or air conditioning equipment is present. Receptacle must be located on the same level and within 25 feet of the equipment.
☐	inside equipment	wiring methods		Receptacles are required if heating or air conditioning equipment is present. Receptacle must be located on the same level and within 25 feet of the equipment.
☐	detached buildings	wiring methods	receptacles, lighting	Receptacle and lighting requirements are the same for attached and detached garages.
☐	equipment grounding conductors			Replacing nongrounding receptacles must be per the requirements for the location and with an approved device using an approved method.
☐	detached buildings	wiring methods	grounding	Where the detached garage is served by only one branch circuit a grounding electrode system is not required. (1 20-amp 120 volt circuit installed for lighting and general use receptacles would not require a ground rod or connection to metal piping.)

Home·Electrical·Wiring

Electrical Codes for Receptacles Pg-5

✓	Location(s)	Category	Device(s)	Description
☐	crawl space	wiring methods	receptacle	All 15 and 20 amp, 120 and 240 volt nonlocking receptacles in wet or damp locations must be listed weather resistant type.
☐	outdoor	wiring methods	receptacle	All 15 and 20 amp, 120 and 240 volt nonlocking receptacles in wet or damp locations must be listed weather resistant type.
☐	outdoor	wiring methods	receptacle cover damp location	Receptacles installed outdoors must have a weatherproof cover or flip cover that is acceptable for damp locations.
☐	outdoor receptacles	wiring methods	cover wet location	Outdoor receptacles in wet locations, unprotected from rainfall must have a cover that is weatherproof whether or not a cord is plugged in. Cover may be the In Use or Bubble type.
☐	all	wiring methods	receptacles	Receptacles are typically mounted 12 inches from the floor to the top of the outlet box.
☐	kitchen	wiring methods common cable types	receptacles	20 Amp Breaker- 12/2 with ground NM Copper

Bedroom AFCI Circuit

Example of a AFCI Bedroom Circuit

A 120 volt grounded receptacle outlet is supplied with three wires: Black Power, White Neutral and Green or Bare Ground. The attachment terminations may be made to screws or quick-connections, depending on the brand receptacle which is selected.

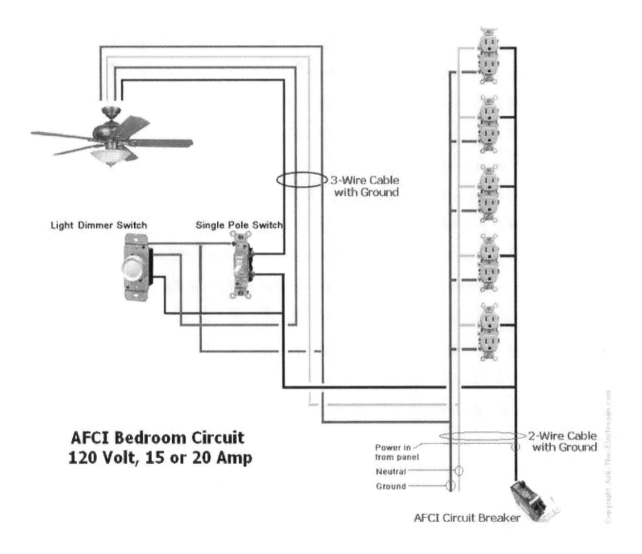

3-Wire Cable with Ground

Light Dimmer Switch

Single Pole Switch

**AFCI Bedroom Circuit
120 Volt, 15 or 20 Amp**

Power in from panel

Neutral

Ground

2-Wire Cable with Ground

AFCI Circuit Breaker

Wiring Note: The bedroom circuit may be wired as either a 15 or 20 amp circuit. The number of outlets is not limited to only five. The circuit may have more depending on the size of the bedroom and the anticipated connected loads placed on the circuit.

Electrical Codes for AFCI Pg-1

✓	Location(s)	Category	Device(s)	Description
☐	rooms	definition	AFCI	A device intended to provide protection from the effects of arc faults by recognizing characteristics unique to arcing and by functioning to deenergize the circuit when an arc-fault is detected.
☐	dwelling unit family rooms, dining rooms, living rooms, parlors, libraries, dens, bedrooms, sunrooms, recreation rooms, closets, hallways	wiring methods	AFCI outlet circuit, individual branch circuit	All 120 volt 15 and 20 amp branch circuits supplying outlets in the required areas shall be protected by a listed AFCI arc-fault circuit interrupter, combination-type, installed to provide protection of the branch circuit. Arc Fault protection may be provided by installing an AFCI receptacle in the first outlet to protection of the branch circuit.
☐	dwelling unit family rooms, dining rooms, living rooms, parlors, libraries, dens, bedrooms, sunrooms, recreation rooms, closets, hallways	wiring methods	AFCI outlet circuit, individual branch circuit	It is permitted to have protection at the first outlet if the wiring method between the circuit breaker and the outlet is RMC, IMC, EMT, MC, or steel-armored cable (type AC) and if metal junction or outlet boxes are used.

Electrical Codes for AFCI Pg-2

✔	Location(s)	Category	Device(s)	Description
☐	dwelling unit family rooms, dining rooms, living rooms, parlors, libraries, dens, bedrooms, sunrooms, recreation rooms, closets, hallways	wiring methods	AFCI outlet circuit, individual branch circuit	All 120 volt 15 and 20 amp branch circuits where the branch circuit is EMT, PVC, ENT, or other listed metal or nonmetallic conduit or tubing which is installed in not less than 2 inches of concrete for the portion of the branch circuit between the branch circuit over current device and the first outlet shall be protected by a listed arc-fault circuit interrupter at the first outlet.
☐	dwelling unit family rooms, dining rooms, living rooms, parlors, libraries, dens, bedrooms, sunrooms, recreation rooms, closets, hallways, stairwell	wiring methods	AFCI outlet circuit	Where the branch circuit wiring has been modified, replaced, or extended, the branch circuit shall be protected by a listed combination-type AFCI that is located at the origin of the branch circuit, or a listed outlet branch-circuit type AFCI located at the first receptacle outlet of the existing branch circuit. All 15 and 20 amp, 120 volt outlets in these rooms and areas must be AFCI protected.
☐	kitchen	wiring methods	AFCI outlet circuit	AFCI protected receptacles are not required in kitchens.
☐	bedroom	wiring methods	smoke detector	120 volt power supply 2-wire NM with ground from AFCI protected circuit.
☐	circuit bedroom	subpanels		All bedroom circuits must be arc-fault protected using AFCI type circuit breakers or AFCI approved receptacle device.

Electrical Codes for AFCI Pg-3

✓	Location(s)	Category	Device(s)	Description
☐		replacement receptacles		AFCI protection is required for replacement receptacles in areas where the circuit requires AFCI protection effective 1/1/2014.
☐		replacement receptacles		AFCI protection may be provided by a circuit breaker, AFCI outlet device, or an upstream AFCI outlet.
☐	all indoor areas	replacement	AFCI receptacle	All 125-volt, 15- and 20- amp receptacle replacements installed in dwelling units shall be listed tamper-resistant as required by 210.12
☐		appliances	air-conditioning	AFCI or LCDI (leakage current detection interrupter) must be provided in the cord or the plug for room air conditioner units.

Electrical Codes for AFCI Pg-4

✓	Location(s)	Category	Device(s)	Description
☐	solar photovoltaic (PV) systems	installation	AFCI direct current	- see below -

Photovoltaic systems with DC source circuits, DC output circuits, or both, on or penetrating a building operating at a PV system maximum voltage of 80 volts or greater shall be protected by a listed (DC) arc-fault circuit interrupter, PV type, or other system components listed to provide equivalent protection.

The PV arc-fault protection means shall comply with the following requirements:
(1.) The system shall detect and interrupt arcing faults resulting from a failure in the intended continuity of a conductor, connection, module, or other system component in the DC PV source and output circuits.
(2.) The system shall disable or disconnect on of the following:
a. Inverters or charge controllers connected to the charge circuit when the fault is detected.
b. System components within the arcing circuit.
(3.) The system shall require that the disabled or disconnected equipment be manually restarted.
(4) The system shall have an annunciator that provides a visual indication that the circuit interrupter has operated. This indication shall not reset automatically.

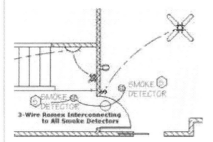

Carbon Monoxide (CO) Alarms

CO Alarms are recommended near bedrooms and sleeping areas where they can wake sleeping residents.

Additional CO alarms are recommended 5-20 feet from sources of CO such as a furnace, water heater or fireplace. Alarms can alert you to a problem only after smoke or CO reach their sensors. Choose locations free of obstructions, where the alarm will stay clean and protected from adverse environmental conditions.

Combination Smoke/CO Alarms

A combination Smoke/CO Alarm makes it easy to provide both types of protection throughout the home. A combination alarm installed on every level of the home is an excellent way to ensure maximum protection for occupants, with a minimum of installation effort.

Heat Alarms

In some areas of the house, it is important to use a heat alarm that senses fire by air temperature, rather than a smoke alarm that senses particles in the air. The installation of heat alarms in attics (finished or unfinished), furnace rooms or garages is recommended, since these locations occasionally experience conditions that can result in improper operation of smoke alarms. Most UL approved heat alarms are designed to alarm when presented with a certain temperature at the alarm. They will not react to smoke and should not be used to replace smoke alarms, but as a supplement to a complete smoke alarm system.

A typical construction project will require a smoke detector in each bedroom and on the ceiling or wall at a point centrally located in the area giving access to bedrooms such as hallways. Mount smoke detectors at least 4 inches from the wall or on the wall with the top of the detector within 4 inches and 12 inches of the highest point of the ceiling. In multi-story units there shall be a detector at each level. Hallways to bedrooms are required to have a smoke detector outside of each sleeping area, and in each bedroom or sleeping area. In new construction when more than one smoke detector is required to be installed within an individual dwelling, the detectors shall be interconnected by installing the electrical wiring in such a manner that the actuation of one alarm will activate all of the alarms in the dwelling.

How to Install Smoke Detectors Pt-2

A 3-wire Romex is installed to each location linking the detectors together. For new installations a size 14-3 can be used. Even though most detectors do not require a ground, always install and bond the ground conductors together and to the box ground connection. Most smoke detectors come with an adapted plate which enables you to use a 1-gang box, 3-0, or 4-0 round box depending on your application.

The 3-wire cables are spliced together.

The smoke detector connector is added to the splice

The connector is now pre-wired for the smoke detector.

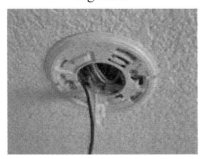

The smoke detector adapter is installed onto the box.

The connector is attached to the smoke detector.

The smoke detector is mounted and the dust cover remains.

When the circuit is powered up the battery is activated.

The indicator lamp shows that the smoke detector has power.

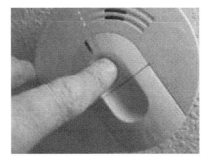

The TEST button is pressed to activate all smoke detectors.

Circuit Design: Smoke Detectors

Example of a Smoke Detector Circuit:

Smoke detectors are best wired as part of an existing lighting circuit, preferably the hallway lights. The normal operation of the hallway lights will ensure that the smoke detector circuit has power and should be operational.

Circuit Design Table: Smoke Detectors		
Device: **Smoke Detector**	**Smoke Detector Symbol**	**Applications:** **Occupied Rooms and Access Areas**
	SD	
Circuit Size: **15 Amps, 120 Volt**	**Cable: Type NM** **14/2, 14/3 w/Grd**	**Box / Enclosure:** **1-Gang or 3-0, Side Nail**

Circuit Notes: Wiring the interconnected smoke detectors requires 3-wire with ground between each smoke detector. A 2-wire with ground may supply the circuit power to the first smoke detector.

Wiring Smoke Detectors

Hardwired Smoke Detectors with 9 Volt Battery Backup

The face of the smoke detector has a TEST button which will activate all the interconnected smoke detectors as if there was an actual alarm.

Smoke Detector Connector:
Smoke detectors typically come with a connector and three lead wires which are then connected to the smoke detector circuit wiring.

It may be best to install smoke detectors of the same brand to ensure total system reliability and compatibility.

Circuit Wiring for Smoke Detectors:
Black is for the circuit power.
White is for the circuit neutral.
Yellow is the alarm circuit which is connected to the red wire of the 3-wire Type NM cable.
This 3-wire circuit interconnects all the smoke detectors to satisfy code requirements.

Wiring Diagram: Smoke Detectors

Wiring Interconnected Smoke Detectors

Smoke detectors are typically wired from a 120 volt lighting circuit. The electrical load of the smoke detectors is minimal and does not require a dedicated circuit.

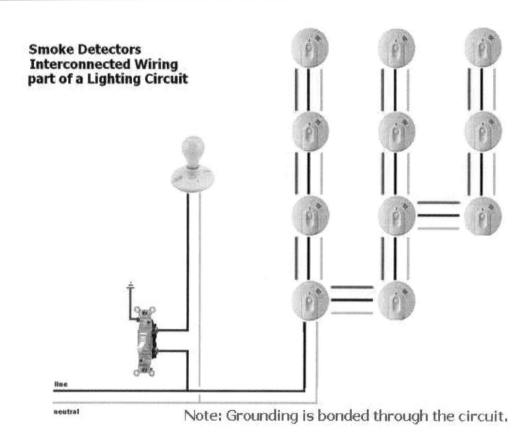

Smoke Detectors Interconnected Wiring part of a Lighting Circuit

line

neutral

Note: Grounding is bonded through the circuit.

Circuit Wiring:

A 2-wire circuit provides power to one smoke detector, and then a 3-wire cable connects all of the other smoke detectors, creating the interconnected alarm capability.

Wiring Note:
It is good to wire the smoke detectors with a lighting circuit to make sure the circuit will be monitored. Interconnected wiring may be connected or extended from any smoked detector to another using a 3-wire Type NM cable.

Electrical Codes for Smoke Detectors Pg-1

✓	Location(s)	Category	Device(s)	Description
☐	bedroom	wiring methods	smoke detector	120 volt power supply 2-wire NM with ground from AFCI protected circuit
☐	rooms	wiring methods	smoke detector	Smoke detectors must be located in each sleeping room.
☐	bedrooms	wiring methods	AFCI outlet circuit	Arc Fault protection required for all outlets, defined by the NEC includes all lighting fixtures, smoke detectors, and receptacles.
☐	hallway	wiring methods	smoke detector	Smoke detectors must be located outside of each sleeping area.
☐	rooms	wiring methods	smoke detector	Smoke detectors must be located on each level of the dwelling unit including basements, but NOT crawl spaces or uninhabitable attics.
☐	rooms	wiring methods	smoke detector	Smoke detectors must be located outside of each sleeping room.
☐	stairwell	wiring methods	smoke detector	Smoke detectors must be located outside of each sleeping area.
☐	in storage area attic areas	when wiring	smoke detectors	Smoke detectors are not required in uninhabitable attics.

Electrical Codes for Smoke Detectors Pg-2

✓	Location(s)	Category	Device(s)	Description
☐	home	wiring methods	smoke detector	Smoke detectors must receive their primary power from the building wiring and be provided with battery backup. Wiring must be permanent and without a disconnecting switch other than a circuit breaker.
☐	boxes	general		Smoke alarms OK on device boxes with 2 #6 screws.
☐		appliances	smoke alarms	NFPA 72 systems OK if permanent part of property.
☐		appliances	smoke alarms	Interconnect so activation of 1 alarm sets off all alarms.
☐		appliances	smoke alarms	Required each story including basements and habitable attics.
☐		appliances	smoke alarms	Battery-only OK alterations or repairs with no access to wire path.
☐	rooms	wiring methods	smoke detector	Smoke detectors located on the ceiling must be no closer than 4 inches from the wall.
☐	rooms	wiring methods	smoke detector	Smoke detectors should be wired with a NM 3-conductor with ground routed to each successive smoke detector so that when the alarm is activated the red conductor carries the signal to all other smoke detectors causing them to activate.

Ceiling Fan Wiring Diagram #1

Wiring Switches for a Ceiling Fan
The power source is located at the switch box.

Ceiling Fan Wiring Diagram

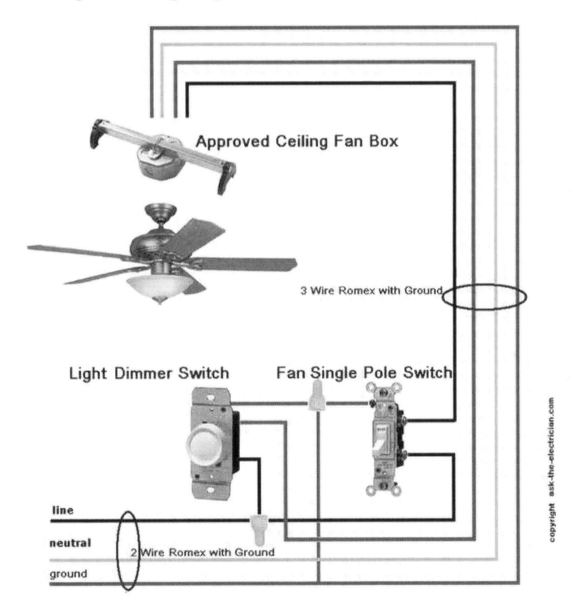

Approved Ceiling Fan Box

3 Wire Romex with Ground

Light Dimmer Switch   Fan Single Pole Switch

line

neutral

ground

2 Wire Romex with Ground

copyright ask-the-electrician.com

Installation Note: The ceiling fan box must be rated for the weight of the ceiling fan. Be sure to maintain 7 feet from the floor to the lowest point of the ceiling fan.

Ceiling Fan Wiring Diagram #2

Wiring Switches for a Ceiling Fan
The power source is located in the ceiling fan box.

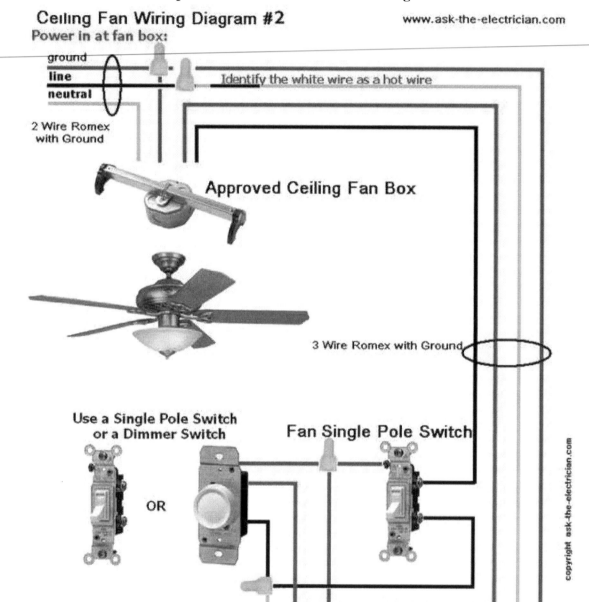

Installation Note: The ceiling fan box must be rated for the weight of the ceiling fan. Be sure to maintain 7 feet from the floor to the lowest point of the ceiling fan.

Electrical Codes for Ceiling Fans

✓	Location(s)	Category	Device(s)	Description
☐	room	wiring methods	ceiling fan	From panelboard or receptacle, power supply with 2-conductor with ground NM cable 120 volt.
☐		appliances	paddle fans	A Paddle Fan greater than 35 lb. and less than 70 lb. must have a fan box that is listed and labeled for suitable weight.
☐		appliances	paddle fans	Boxes must be listed for paddle fan support (no standard boxes may be used).
☐		appliances	paddle fans	Independent means of support must be provided for fans greater than 70 lb.
☐		appliances	paddle fans	Paddle fans up to 35 lbs may be installed with listed boxes without a weight marking.
☐	boxes	general		Paddle fans or ceiling fans require a listed and labeled paddle fan or ceiling fan box.
☐	rooms	wiring methods	ceiling fans	Outlet box listed for support specification for ceiling fans.
☐		lighting	tub & shower areas	No cord connected or pendant luminaires, lighting track, or ceiling suspended paddle fans may be installed in the first 8 foot area above the tub rim or shower threshold and for the zone extending 3 feet outside of the area.
☐	bathroom	lighting	lighting	No part of a lighting track, hanging lighting fixture or ceiling fan is allowed within a 3 feet horizontal by 8 feet vertical zone above the threshold of a shower or the rim of a bathtub. Recessed or surface mounted fixtures are allowed in this zone but must be listed for damp locations.

Wiring Single Pole Switches

Wiring a 120 Volt Single Pole Switch

The front and back of a 15A 120V single pole switch, and the wiring connections of the screw terminals. When the white wire is used for switching it is identified with black tape or permanent marker.

Wiring Note:
The black wire of the incoming power source attaches to one of the brass screw terminals and the black wire of the cable leading to the light fixture connects to the other brass screw terminal. Quick connect terminations may be made with 15 amp switches and #14 gauge solid wire. The circuit ground is attached to the green terminal screw.

Wiring Diagram: Single Switch #1

Wiring a Single Switch
The power source is located at the switch box.

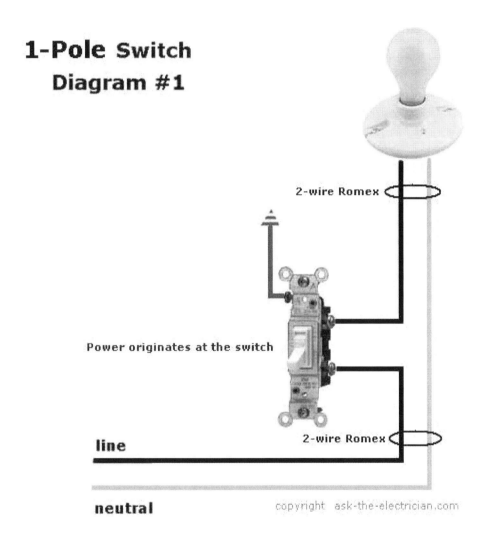

1-Pole Switch

Diagram #1

2-wire Romex

Power originates at the switch

line

2-wire Romex

neutral

copyright ask-the-electrician.com

Wiring Diagram: Single Switch #2

Wiring a Single Switch
The power source is located at the fixture box.

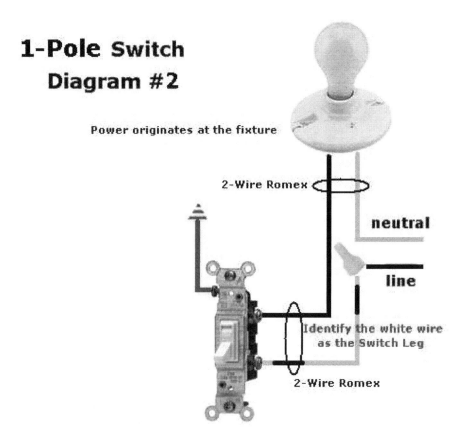

1-Pole Switch
Diagram #2

Power originates at the fixture

2-Wire Romex

neutral

line

Identify the white wire
as the Switch Leg

2-Wire Romex

copyright ask-the-electrician.com

Electrical Codes for 3 Way and 4-Way Switches

✓	Location(s)	Category	Device(s)	Description
☐	hallway	wiring methods	lighting	Wall switch controlled lighting outlet is required.
☐	stairwell	wiring methods	lighting	Where there are 6 or more risers on the stairs, a wall switch to control the lighting outlet is required at each level. 3-way or 4-way switching is required.
☐	detached buildings garages outbuildings			The exceptions are 3-way or snap switches that are allowed in outbuildings or garages.
☐		old wiring	knob & tube	A bushing is permitted for knob and tube wiring at the termination point of a raceway to open switchboards.
☐	rooms & halls	wiring methods	switch 4-way	Splice neutral wires in switch boxes, do not switch neutrals.
☐		switches		All switch wiring must be wired using ungrounded conductors except in a raceway that has sufficient room to add a neutral.

Wiring 3-Way Switches

Two 3-Way switches are used to control
one or more light fixtures from two locations.

The front of a 3-Way Toggle Switch	The back of a 3-Way Toggle Switch revealing the wire terminal connections.

Wiring Note:
The single darker screw terminal that is found at one end of the switch is the Point. The wire of the power in and the wire that leads to the light fixtures are attached to the Point screw terminals.
The two screw terminals at the opposite end of the switch are the Travelers. Two wires are connected to these screw terminals at both switch locations.
The circuit ground is attached to the green terminal screw of each switch.

Wiring 3-Way Switches

Eight Wiring Methods Outlined

Identifying the cables found at each box location for each wiring method.

Identifying 3-Way Switch Variations

Note: #14 Romex is being used for these examples. Please match your wire gauge.

Method #	3-Way Switch #1	3-Way Switch #2	Light Fixture #1	Light Fixture #2	Outlet #1
1	14/2 - Power In 14/2 - Light #1 14/3 - Switch #2	14/3 - Switch #1	14/2 - Switch #1	n/a	n/a
2	14/3 - Switch #1	14/3 - Switch #1 14/2 - Light #1	14/2 - Power In 14/3 - Switch #2	n/a	n/a
3	14/2 - Power In 14/3 - Light #1	14/3 - Light #1	14/3 - Switch #1 14/3 - Switch #2 14/2 - Light #2	14/2 - Light #1	n/a
4	14/2 - Power In 14/3 - Light #1	14/3 - Light #1	14/3 - Switch #1 14/3 - Switch #2	n/a	n/a
5	14/3 - Light #1	14/3 - Light #1	14/3 - Switch #1 14/3 - Switch #2 14/2 - Power In	n/a	n/a
6	14/2 - Power In 14/3 - Switch #2	14/3 - Switch #1 14/2 - Light #1	14/2 - Switch #1	n/a	n/a
7	14/2 - Power In 14/3 - Light #1	14/3 - Light #1	14/3 - Switch #1 14/3 - Switch #2 14/2 - Outlet #1	n/a	14/2 - Light #1
8	14/2 - Power In 14/3 - Switch #2	14/3 - Switch #1 14/2 - Outlet #1	n/a	n/a	14/2 - Switch #2

Wiring Diagram: 3-Way Switches #1

Wiring Method:
The power source enters the first 3-Way switch box.
First switch box feeds power to the light fixture.
A 3-wire cable feeds the second 3-Way switch box.

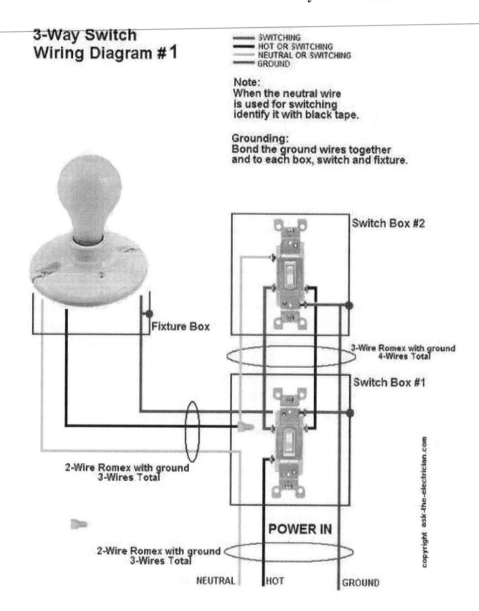

3-Way Switch
Wiring Diagram #1

SWITCHING
HOT OR SWITCHING
NEUTRAL OR SWITCHING
GROUND

Note:
When the neutral wire
is used for switching
identify it with black tape.

Grounding:
Bond the ground wires together
and to each box, switch and fixture.

Fixture Box

Switch Box #2

3-Wire Romex with ground
4-Wires Total

Switch Box #1

2-Wire Romex with ground
3-Wires Total

POWER IN

copyright ask-the-electrician.com

2-Wire Romex with ground
3-Wires Total

NEUTRAL   HOT   GROUND

NOTE: New electrical wiring requires that a neutral wire must be provided in the switch box.

Wiring Diagram: 3-Way Switches #2

Wiring Method:
The power source enters the light fixture.
A 2-wire cable connects the light to the first 3-Way switch box.
A 3-wire cable connects between the first and the second 3-Way switch boxes.

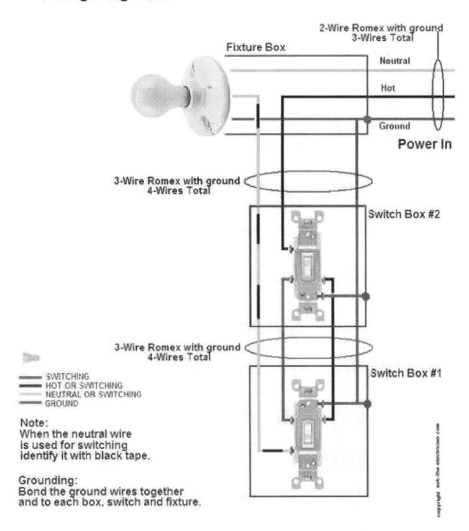

3-Way Switch
Wiring Diagram #2

2-Wire Romex with ground
3-Wires Total

Fixture Box

Neutral

Hot

Ground

Power In

3-Wire Romex with ground
4-Wires Total

Switch Box #2

3-Wire Romex with ground
4-Wires Total

Switch Box #1

SWITCHING
HOT OR SWITCHING
NEUTRAL OR SWITCHING
GROUND

Note:
When the neutral wire
is used for switching
identify it with black tape.

Grounding:
Bond the ground wires together
and to each box, switch and fixture.

NOTE: New electrical wiring requires that a neutral wire must be provided in the switch box.

Wiring Diagram: 3-Way Switches #3

Wiring Method:
The power source enters the first 3-Way Switch box.
A 3-wire cable travels to the light fixture box.
A 3-wire cable travels from the light fixture box to the 2nd switch box.
The wiring configurations in the fixture box are crucial.
Notice that the first light fixture may feed additional light fixtures.

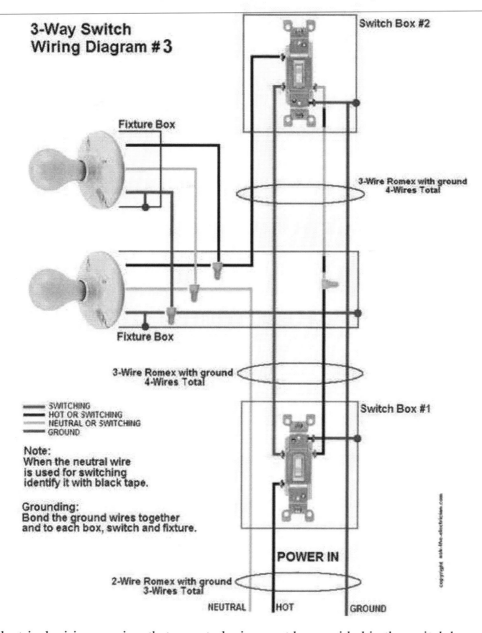

3-Way Switch Wiring Diagram #3

Switch Box #2

Fixture Box

3-Wire Romex with ground
4-Wires Total

Fixture Box

3-Wire Romex with ground
4-Wires Total

SWITCHING
HOT OR SWITCHING
NEUTRAL OR SWITCHING
GROUND

Switch Box #1

Note:
When the neutral wire
is used for switching
identify it with black tape.

Grounding:
Bond the ground wires together
and to each box, switch and fixture.

POWER IN

2-Wire Romex with ground
3-Wires Total

NEUTRAL   HOT   GROUND

NOTE: New electrical wiring requires that a neutral wire must be provided in the switch box.

Wiring Diagram: 3-Way Switches #4

Wiring Method:
The power source enters the first 3-Way switch box.
A 3-wire cable travels to the light fixture box.
A 3-wire cable travels from the light fixture box to the 2nd switch box.
The wiring configurations in the fixture box are crucial.
Notice that there is only one light fixture.

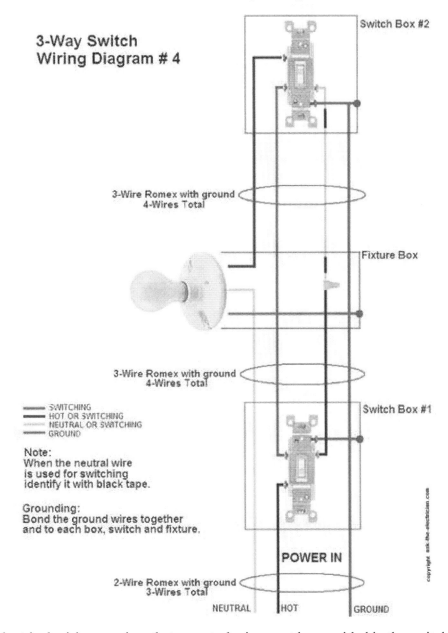

3-Way Switch
Wiring Diagram # 4

Switch Box #2

3-Wire Romex with ground
4-Wires Total

Fixture Box

3-Wire Romex with ground
4-Wires Total

SWITCHING
HOT OR SWITCHING
NEUTRAL OR SWITCHING
GROUND

Switch Box #1

Note:
When the neutral wire
is used for switching
identify it with black tape.

Grounding:
Bond the ground wires together
and to each box, switch and fixture.

POWER IN

2-Wire Romex with ground
3-Wires Total

NEUTRAL   HOT   GROUND

NOTE: New electrical wiring requires that a neutral wire must be provided in the switch box.

Wiring Diagram: 3-Way Switches #5

Wiring Method:
The power source enters the light fixture.
A 3-wire cable connects the light to the 1st and 2nd 3-Way switch boxes.
The wiring configurations in the fixture box are crucial.

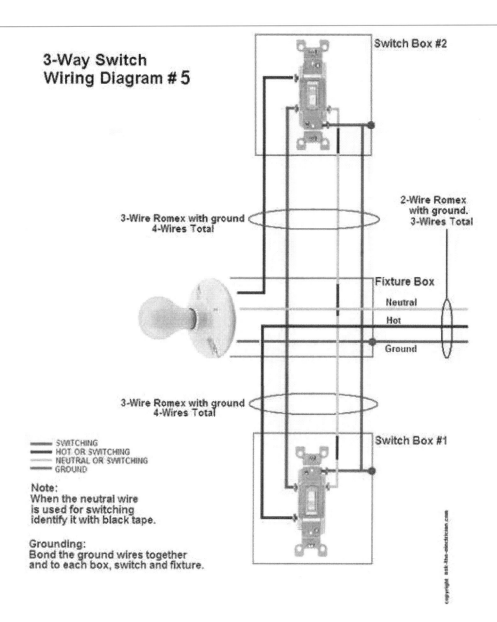

3-Way Switch
Wiring Diagram # 5

Switch Box #2

3-Wire Romex with ground
4-Wires Total

2-Wire Romex
with ground.
3-Wires Total

Fixture Box
Neutral
Hot
Ground

3-Wire Romex with ground
4-Wires Total

Switch Box #1

SWITCHING
HOT OR SWITCHING
NEUTRAL OR SWITCHING
GROUND

Note:
When the neutral wire
is used for switching
identify it with black tape.

Grounding:
Bond the ground wires together
and to each box, switch and fixture.

copyright ask-the-electrian.com

NOTE: New electrical wiring requires that a neutral wire must be provided in the switch box.

Wiring Diagram: 3-Way Switches #6

Wiring Method:
The power source enters the first 3-Way switch box.
A 3-wire cable connects the 1st and 2nd switch boxes.
A 2-wire cable connects the light fixture to the 2nd switch box.

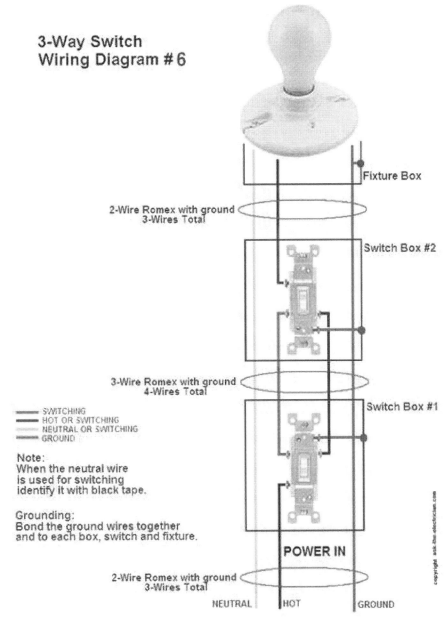

3-Way Switch
Wiring Diagram # 6

Fixture Box

2-Wire Romex with ground
3-Wires Total

Switch Box #2

3-Wire Romex with ground
4-Wires Total

SWITCHING
HOT OR SWITCHING
NEUTRAL OR SWITCHING
GROUND

Switch Box #1

Note:
When the neutral wire
is used for switching
identify it with black tape.

Grounding:
Bond the ground wires together
and to each box, switch and fixture.

POWER IN

2-Wire Romex with ground
3-Wires Total

NEUTRAL   HOT   GROUND

NOTE: New electrical wiring requires that a neutral wire must be provided in the switch box.

Home·Electrical·Wiring

Wiring Diagram: 3-Way Switches #7

Wiring Method:
The power source enters the first 3-Way switch box.
A 3-wire cable travels to the light fixture box.
A 3-wire cable travels from the light fixture box to the 2nd switch box.
The wiring configurations in the fixture box are crucial.
Notice that the light fixture also feeds a wall outlet which is controlled as well.

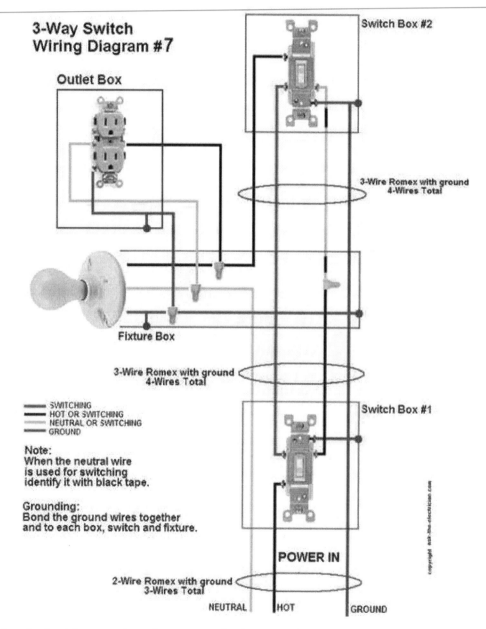

3-Way Switch
Wiring Diagram #7

Outlet Box

Switch Box #2

3-Wire Romex with ground
4-Wires Total

Fixture Box

3-Wire Romex with ground
4-Wires Total

SWITCHING
HOT OR SWITCHING
NEUTRAL OR SWITCHING
GROUND

Switch Box #1

Note:
When the neutral wire
is used for switching
identify it with black tape.

Grounding:
Bond the ground wires together
and to each box, switch and fixture.

POWER IN

2-Wire Romex with ground
3-Wires Total

NEUTRAL   HOT   GROUND

NOTE: New electrical wiring requires that a neutral wire must be provided in the switch box.

—Home·Electrical·Wiring—

Wiring Diagram: 3-Way Switches #8

Wiring Method:
The power source enters the first 3-Way switch box.
A 3-wire cable connects the 1st and 2nd switch boxes.
A 2-wire cable connects a wall outlet to the 2nd switch box.

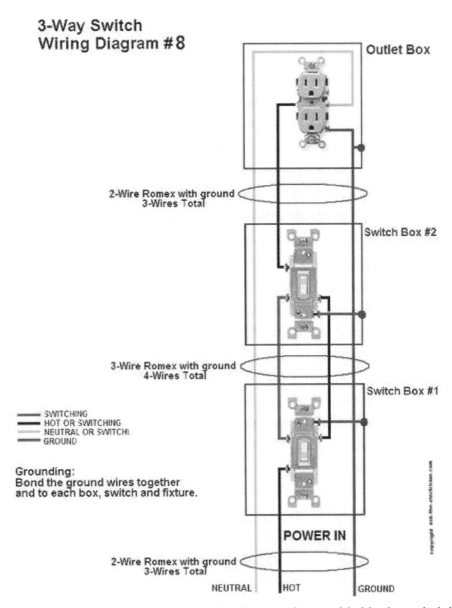

3-Way Switch
Wiring Diagram #8

Outlet Box

2-Wire Romex with ground
3-Wires Total

Switch Box #2

3-Wire Romex with ground
4-Wires Total

Switch Box #1

SWITCHING
HOT OR SWITCHING
NEUTRAL OR SWITCHI.
GROUND

Grounding:
Bond the ground wires together
and to each box, switch and fixture.

POWER IN

2-Wire Romex with ground
3-Wires Total

NEUTRAL   HOT   GROUND

NOTE: New electrical wiring requires that a neutral wire must be provided in the switch box.

Wiring 4-Way Switches

One or more 4 -Way switches may be used along with a pair of 3-way switches to control one or more light fixtures from multiple switch locations.

The front of a 4-Way Toggle Switch

The back of a 4-Way Toggle Switch
revealing the wire terminal connections.

Wiring Note:
There are two pairs of screws on each end of the 4-way switch, each pair having a different color to help identify them.

These two screw terminals at the opposite ends of the 4-way switch are an extension of the 3-way switch travelers.

Two wires are connected to each pair of screw terminals at each end of the switch.

The circuit ground is attached to the green terminal screw of each switch.

Wiring Diagram: 4-Way Switches #1

Wiring Method:
The power source enters the first 3-Way switch box.
A 3-wire cable connects to the 4-Way switch.
A 3-wire cable connects to the second 3-Way switch.
A 2-wire cable connects to the light fixture.

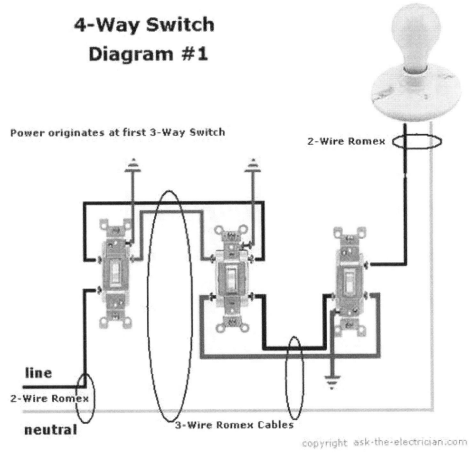

NOTE: New electrical wiring requires that a neutral wire must be provided in the switch box.

Wiring Diagram: 4-Way Switches #2

Wiring Method:
The power source enters the light fixture box.
A 2-wire cable connects the first 3-Way switch box.
A 3-wire cable connects the 4-Way switch box.
A 3-wire cable connects to the second 3-Way switch box.

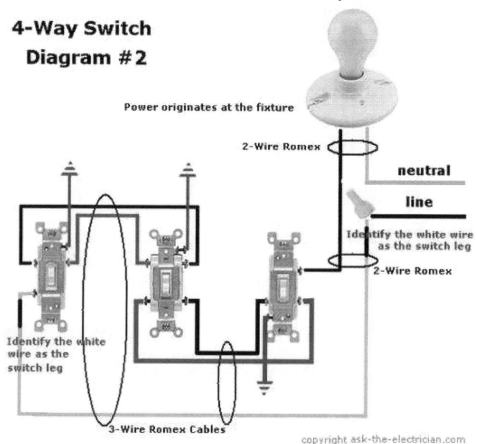

NOTE: New electrical wiring requires that a neutral wire must be provided in the switch box.

Electrical Codes for Dimmer Switches

✓	Location(s)	Category	Device(s)	Description
☐		switches		Dimmers may only be used for incandescent lights not receptacles.
☐		switches		Snap switches and dimmers are required to be grounded.

Home·Electrical·Wiring

Wiring Diagram: Bathroom Exhaust Fan

Wiring Switches for a Bathroom Exhaust Fan.
Bathroom exhaust fan and light with separate switches.
Provision for occupancy switch to turn off the exhaust fan automatically.

Bathroom Exhaust Fan with Two Switches
*Spare neutral for Occupancy Switch

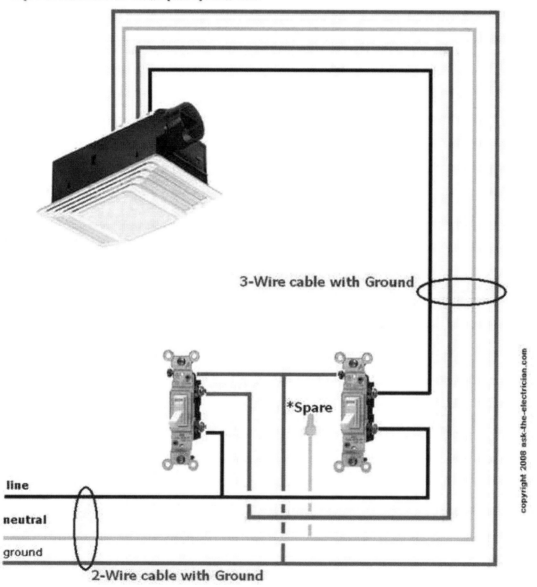

3-Wire cable with Ground

*Spare

line

neutral

ground

copyright 2008 ask-the-electrician.com

2-Wire cable with Ground

Wiring Note: The combination exhaust fan and light may be shared with another light circuit; however additional features such as heat lamps or heating elements may require a dedicated circuit.

Electrical Codes for Bath Vent Fan

✓	Location(s)	Category	Device(s)	Description
☐	bathrooms	GFCI	vent fans exhaust fans	Vent fans installed directly above showers must be GFCI protected per manufacturer's instructions.
☐	hydromassage bathtubs Jacuzzi	GFCI	vent fans exhaust fans	Vent fans installed directly above showers must be GFCI protected per manufacturers' instructions.
☐	bathroom	20 amp circuit		No other device allowed on the receptacle circuit unless the dedicated 20 amp circuit supplies only one bathroom, such as lights, vent fans etc.

Electrical Codes for Furnace

✓	Location(s)	Category	Device(s)	Description
☐	central furnace	appliances		The central furnace system includes all associated equipment (electrostatic filters, pumps, etc).
☐	central furnace	appliances		The central furnace must be on an individual circuit.
☐		appliances	electric furnaces and space heaters	An appliance unit switch that opens all ungrounded conductors is permitted as a disconnect for a space heater with a motor that is not greater than 1/8 hp.
☐	rooms	appliances	electric furnaces and space heaters	An appliance disconnect means must be in sight or there must be a lockable circuit breaker.
☐		appliances	electric furnaces and space heaters	An appliance branch circuit must be 125% of the load (heat watts + motor)

Electrical Codes for Vacuum System

✓	Location(s)	Category	Device(s)	Description
☐		appliances	central vacuum	A central vacuum system rating must not be greater than 80% of the individual branch circuit rating, or 50% of a multi-outlet branch circuit rating.
☐	garage	wiring	receptacles GFCI exception #2	GFCI protection is not required for receptacles within dedicated space for appliances that are not easily moved. This applies to single receptacles for a refrigerator or vacuum system, a duplex receptacle for a refrigerator and a freezer. GFCI devices must be installed in a readily accessible location.
☐		appliances	central vacuum	A central vacuum system cord must have the same ampacity as the branch circuit.
☐		appliances	central vacuum	Bond all non-current-carrying metal parts of a central vacuum system.

Electrical Codes for Jacuzzi Tub

✓	Location(s)	Category	Device(s)	Description
☐	hydromassage bathtubs Jacuzzi	GFCI	vent fans exhaust fans	Vent fans installed directly above showers must be GFCI protected per manufacturer's instructions.
☐	hydromassage bathtubs Jacuzzi	receptacles	tamper resistant	All 15 and 20 amp 120 volt receptacle outlets in dwelling units shall be listed tamper-resistant.
☐	hydromassage bathtubs Jacuzzi	GFCI		Hydro-massage bathtub electrical equipment must be GFCI protected and should be on a dedicated 20 amp circuit.
☐	hydromassage bathtubs Jacuzzi	circuit	20 amp circuit	Hydro-massage bathtub electrical equipment must be GFCI protected and should be on a dedicated 20 amp circuit.
☐	hydromassage bathtubs Jacuzzi	access		Access is required to all electrical equipment for hydromassage bathtubs.
☐	hydromassage bathtubs Jacuzzi	grounding	pump motor	All metal piping systems and all grounded metal parts must be bonded to the pump motor with #8 solid copper wire that shall be terminated to the equipment grounding conductor of the branch circuit of the motor.

Wiring Multi-Wire Circuits

Many 240 volt circuits are fed from a 2-pole circuit breaker, however sometimes terminations are made incorrectly which may produce incorrect voltage and may even be a code violation.

Correct Wiring of a Multi-Wire Circuit.

An indication of a multi-wire circuit is when a black and red wire are terminated circuit breakers that are side by side as they should be, however the configuration can be made incorrectly as shown in the photos below.

Incorrect Multi-Wiring Circuit Breaker Configuration

Terminating to two full size breakers is correct; however a tie bar does not tie the handles together of the circuit breakers. A tie bar should be installed on the circuit breakers or a 2-pole circuit breaker should be installed.

Terminating both circuit conductors to a twin or tandem circuit breaker will not produce two separate circuits producing 240 volts, but instead two 120 volt circuits off the same buss. This practice is also incorrect because of the potential for overloading the neutral wire if the circuit is a 3-wire 120/240 volt circuit.

Note: If the panel permits, a quad circuit breaker may be installed into the space of two full size circuit breakers therefore providing four circuits. Two 240 volt circuits may be configured when the circuits are positioned in the inside and outside positions of the quad circuit breaker with tie bars or handles.

240 Volt 4-Wire Receptacle

Wiring a 120/240 Volt 4-Wire Receptacle Outlet
A 240 volt circuit has two 120 volt circuits, that's why the receptacle says 120/250V.
A 240 volt circuit will range between 220-250 volts from the electric utility company.

The front of a 4-Wire 30A 250V receptacle

The back of a 4-Wire 30A 250V receptacle describing the wire terminal connections.

14-30R

FRONT / FACE

4-WIRE HOOK UP

Wiring Note: The red wire and the black wire may be in either the X or Y terminal; it does not matter for 240 volt wiring.

240 Volt 3-Wire Receptacle

Wiring a 120/240 Volt 3-Wire Receptacle Outlet
A 240 volt circuit has two 120 volt circuits, that's why the receptacle says 120/250V.
A 240 volt circuit will range between 220-250 volts from the electric utility company.

The front of a 3-Wire 30A 250V receptacle

The back of a 3-Wire 30A 250V receptacle describing the wire terminal connections.

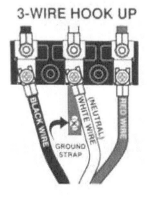

Wiring Note: The red wire and the black wire may be in either the X or Y terminal; it does not matter for 240 volt wiring.

Circuit Design: 50 Amp 240 Volt Range

For new circuits a 50 amp 4-Wire 250 Volt receptacle outlet circuit will be found in the kitchen for the freestanding all electric range.

Circuit Design Table: 50 Amp 250 Volt Range		
Device: **50 Amp 250 Volt** **4-Wire Receptacle**	**240 Volt Outlet Symbol**	**Application:** **Kitchen**
Circuit Size: **50 Amps, 240 Volt**	**Cable: Romex** **8/3 Cu. w/ Grd**	**Box / Enclosure:** **2-Gang, Side Nail**

Circuit Notes:

A 50 Amp 240 Volt circuit is commonly installed for the free standing electric kitchen range.

Typical Electrical Cables:

8/3 Copper with ground or 6/3 Aluminum with ground.

Voltage Terminology:

You may notice that 240 and 250 is used when describing the voltage for this electrical circuit. For example the receptacle is "rated' for 250 volts, however the home circuit will typically test at 230 to 240 volts.

Electrical Codes for Kitchen Range Pg-1

✓	Location(s)	Category	Device(s)	Description
☐	kitchen	circuit	range	Ranges rated 8750 watts or more must be supplied by a minimum 40 amp circuit.
☐	kitchen	branch circuits		Receptacles may be used for a clock or a gas range ignition.
☐	kitchen	counter	receptacles	The area behind a sink or range is considered countertop space if 12 inches or greater to the wall or 18 inches or greater to a corner.
☐	kitchen counters	wiring methods	receptacles	Counter spaces divided by range tops, refrigerators, or sinks must be considered separate spaces.
☐	rooms, kitchen	wiring methods	countertop receptacles	Receptacle outlets shall be located on, or above, but not more than 20 inches above the countertop. Receptacle outlet assemblies listed for the application shall be permitted to be installed in countertops. Receptacle outlets rendered not readily accessible by appliances fastened in place, appliance garages, sinks, or range tops, or appliances occupying dedicated space shall not be considered as these required outlets.
☐	kitchen	equipment grounding conductors	range free standing	Existing ranges and dryers must have an Equipment Ground Conductor.
☐	kitchen	circuit 4-wire	range free standing	4-wire circuit required for cord and plug connected free standing ranges. Typically wired with 50 amp circuit, #6/3 with ground CU NM Cable.

Electrical Codes for Kitchen Range Pg-2

✓	Location(s)	Category	Device(s)	Description
☐	kitchen	range hoods	receptacles	Range hoods and built in microwaves may be cord connected if the receptacle is accessible and not supplied from an individual circuit. (Microwave ovens are usually supplied by a dedicated 20 amp circuit, 12/2 with ground CU NM cable.)
☐	kitchen	wiring methods common cable types	range-freestanding-40-amp	40 Amp Breaker- 8/3 with ground NM Copper 6/3 with ground SER Aluminum
☐	kitchen	wiring methods common cable types	range-freestanding-50-amp	50 Amp Breaker- 8/3 with ground NM Copper 6/3 with ground SER Aluminum

Circuit Design: 240 Volt Stove

 Stove circuits are typically 240 volt; however the amperage will depend on the exact size oven that will be installed.

Circuit Design Table: Stove		
Device: **240 Volt, Hardwired**	**240 Volt Outlet Symbol**	**Application:** **Kitchen**
Circuit Size: **240 Volt**	**Cable: Type NM** **8/3 Cu. w/ Grd**	**Box / Enclosure:** **2-Gang, Side Nail**

Circuit Notes: The size of the stove circuit will depend on the exact oven that is to be installed. Consult the installation manual or the manufacturer's specifications for the specific circuit voltage and amperage.

Different Types of Stoves:

Conventional Single Cook Top Stove.

Dual Gas and Electric Stove.

Jenn-Air with Down Draft Exhaust Fan.

Some stoves or cook tops may have an optional down draft exhaust fan which may require extending circuit power or a switch control to the location of the external exhaust fan.

Booster Fans: Due to a long length of exhaust ducting and or number of bends within the exhaust duct an external booster exhaust fan may be required which will require circuit power and control capability from the stove or cook top unit.

Electrical Codes for Kitchen Cook Top Pg-1

✓	Location(s)	Category	Device(s)	Description
☐	kitchen cooktop	wiring methods	receptacles	If spacing behind the cooktop is 18 inches or greater, this area must be counted as wall space and receptacles must be installed so that no point along the countertop is further than 2 feet from a receptacle (or 1 receptacle every 4 feet)
☐	kitchen island	wiring methods	receptacles	An island requires a receptacle only if larger than 24 inches by 12 inches. If a sink or cooktop is installed on the island and the width of the counter behind the appliance is less than 12 inches a receptacle must be installed on both sides. (Locate receptacle no more than 12 inches below cabinet.)
☐	kitchen peninsula	wiring methods	receptacles	A peninsula requires a receptacle only if larger than 24 inches by 12 inches. If a sink or cooktop is installed on the island and the width of the counter behind the appliance is less than 12 inches a receptacle must be installed on both sides. (Locate receptacle no more than 12 inches below cabinet.)
☐	kitchen cooktop	wiring methods	receptacles	If spacing behind the cooktop is less than 18 inches one receptacle is required within 2 feet of each side of the cooktop.

Electrical Codes for Kitchen Cook Top Pg-2

✓	Location(s)	Category	Device(s)	Description
☐	kitchen	wiring methods common cable types	cooktop-30-amp	30 Amp Breaker- 10/3 with ground NM Copper 8/3 with ground SER Aluminum
☐	kitchen	wiring methods common cable types	cooktop-40-amp	40 Amp Breaker- 8/3 with ground NM Copper 6/3 with ground SER Aluminum
☐	kitchen	wiring methods common cable types	cooktop-50-amp	50 Amp Breaker- 8/3 with ground NM Copper 6/3 with ground SER Aluminum

Circuit Design: 240 Volt Oven

 Oven circuits are typically 240 volt; however the amperage size will depend on the exact oven that will be installed.

Circuit Design Table: Oven		
Device: 240 Volt, Hardwired	**240 Volt Outlet Symbol**	**Application:** Kitchen
Circuit Size: 20 Amps, 240 Volt	**Cable: Romex** 12/2 Cu. w/ Grd.	**Box / Enclosure:** 1-Gang, Side Nail

Circuit Notes:
The size of the oven circuit will depend on the exact oven that is to be installed.
Different Types of Ovens:
Conventional Single Oven, Double Oven, Single Oven and Microwave Combination, Self Cleaning Oven.
Consult the installation manual or the manufacturer's specifications for the specific circuit voltage and amperage.

Electrical Codes for Kitchen Oven

✓	Location(s)	Category	Device(s)	Description
☐	kitchen	appliances		Cord and plug ovens and cooking units are permitted if they are listed and labeled.
☐	kitchen	range hoods	receptacles	Range hoods and built in microwaves may be cord connected if the receptacle is accessible and not supplied from an individual circuit. (Microwave ovens are usually supplied by a dedicated 20 amp circuit, 12/2 with ground CU NM cable.)
☐	kitchen	wiring methods common cable types	oven-30-amp	30 Amp Breaker- 10/3 with ground NM Copper 8/3 with ground SER Aluminum
☐	kitchen	wiring methods common cable types	oven-40-amp	40 Amp Breaker- 8/3 with ground NM Copper 6/3 with ground SER Aluminum
☐	kitchen	wiring methods common cable types	oven-50amp	50 Amp Breaker- 8/3 with ground NM Copper 6/3 with ground SER Aluminum

Home·Electrical·Wiring

Circuit Design: 240 Volt Clothes Dryer

 Clothes dryers are either gas or electric, and many new homes are equipped for both types, therefore two circuits will be required.

Circuit Design Table: Dryer		
Device: **30 Amp, 240 Volt** **4-Wire Receptacle**	**240 Volt Outlet Symbol**	**Application:** **Laundry**
Circuit Size: **30 Amp, 240 Volt**	**Cable: Type NM** **10/3 Cu. w/ Grd**	**Box / Enclosure:** **2-Gang, Side Nail**

Circuit Notes:
The size of the electric clothes dryer circuit is commonly 30 amps, 240 volts. When the dryer is gas then a 20 amp 120 volt circuit is installed, and depending on the location the 120 volt circuit may be shared. (See the 120 volt Circuit Design Table.) Some locations may require that both circuits are installed so the home may be equipped with either a gas or all electric clothes dryer.

Different Types of Clothes Dryers: All Electric - Electric motor and electric heating.

Gas - Requires a 120 volt outlet for the motor, and the gas pluming for the heat.

Stack Units and Combo Units: Often found in apartments, condos, timeshares, and modular homes. Stack units are two separate units that are stacked on top of each other; one is the clothes washer and the other the clothes dryer. Typically because these are two separate units, stack units require two separate circuits, one for each unit. A Combo Unit is typically one unit with both the clothes washer and the clothes dryer and requires only one electrical circuit. Some Stack Units or Combo Units may be having either gas or electric heating for the dryer, which will have an affect on the circuit size. Consult the installation manual or the manufacturer's specifications for the specific circuit voltage and amperage.

Home·Electrical·Wiring

Electrical Codes for Clothes Dryer

✓	Location(s)	Category	Device(s)	Description
☐	laundry room	branch circuits and outlets	receptacles	A 30A circuit is the minimum requirement for an electric dryer which is wired with 10 AWG Cu, or 8 AWG AL.
☐	kitchen	equipment grounding conductors	range free standing	Existing ranges and dryers must have an Equipment Ground Conductor.
☐	laundry room	circuit 4-wire	outlet receptacle	4-wire 30 amp circuit is required for electric dryers.
☐	laundry room	branch circuits and outlets	receptacles	An electric dryer requires a 4-conductor branch circuit.
☐		cable systems	service entrance and underground SE	An insulated neutral conductor (type SE-R) is required except for existing dryers or existing feeders to a building with no other continuous metal path.
☐	laundry	wiring methods common cable types	dryer-clothes	30 Amp Breaker- 10/3 with ground NM Copper

Circuit Design: 240 Volt Water Heater

Conventional tank type water heaters are either gas or electric and are found in the garage, utility room or laundry room.

Circuit Design Table: Water Heater		
Device: Hardwired Flex Conduit	240 Volt Outlet Symbol	Application: Garage or Utility Room
Circuit Size: 30 Amp, 240 Volt	Cable: Romex 10/2 Cu. w/ Grd	Box / Enclosure: 1-Gang, Side Nail

Circuit Notes:

The size of the electric water heater circuit is commonly 30 amps, 240 volts; the circuit consists of two circuit conductors and a ground. When using a Romex type cable the insulated white conductor must be identified with black or red electrical tape or a permanent marker. At this time 240 volt electric water heaters do not require a neutral wire, however this may change in the near future.

In some locations there may be a gas or electric water heater which will require a booster assisted exhaust fan which is typically 120 volts.

Electrical Codes for Water Heater

✓	Location(s)	Category	Device(s)	Description
☐	garage	wiring methods common cable types	water heater-30 amp	30 Amp Breaker- 10/2 with ground NM Copper
☐	utility room	wiring	cable	Use 10/2 with ground NM Copper for water heaters.
☐	utility room	panel	circuit	30 Amp Breaker for water heater.

Circuit Design: 240 Volt HVAC Compressor

HVAC - Heating Ventilation and Air Conditioning units are not complete without an external compressor unit and circuit disconnect.

Circuit Design Table: Air Conditioning		
Device: Hardwired Circuit	**240 Volt Outlet Symbol**	**Application:** Exterior
		COMP AND DISC.
Circuit Size: 240 Volt	**Cable: Romex** 2-Wire Cu. w/ Grd	**Box / Enclosure:** Disconnect Switch

Circuit Notes: The size of the air conditioning circuit will depend on the exact size of the AC unit that is to be installed. The size of the AC unit will depend on the size of the home and the energy efficiency factors.

Typical Electrical Cables: 2-Wire copper or aluminum with ground.

Note: Some air conditioning manufacturers may not allow aluminum conductors to be used. Consult the HVAC contractor or the installation manual for the electrical circuit specifications.

Electrical Codes for Air Conditioner

✓	Location(s)	Category	Device(s)	Description
☐		appliances	air-conditioning	A working space is required in front of an air conditioning disconnect switch.
☐	crawl space	wiring methods		Receptacles are required if heating or air conditioning equipment is present. Receptacle must be located on the same level and within 25 feet of the equipment.
☐	in storage area attic areas	when wiring	receptacles	Receptacles are permitted but not required unless heating or air conditioning equipment is located in the storage area.
☐	inside equipment	wiring methods		Receptacles are required if heating or air conditioning equipment is present. Receptacle must be located on the same level and within 25 feet of the equipment.
☐	crawl space	wiring methods	lighting	Lighting outlet or fixture is required if space is used for storage or contains equipment that may need servicing. Light must be located at or near the equipment. This applies to equipment such as heating or air conditioning.
☐		appliances	air-conditioning	A room air conditioning plug disconnect is permitted if it controls 6 feet or less of floor.

Circuit Design: 120 Volt GFCI Receptacle Outdoor

Example of a 120 Volt GFCI:
An exterior outlet must be located at the front and rear entrances to the home providing GFCI protection and a weatherproof cover.

Circuit Design Table: 120 Volt GFCI		
Device: GFCI Receptacle	**GFCI Outlet Symbol**	**Applications:** Front and Rear Entrances
	GFCI	
Circuit Size: 20 Amps, 120 Volt	**Cable:** #12 THWN	**Box / Enclosure:** 1-Gang, Weather Proof Box

Wiring Notes:
When the electrical wiring is being installed in the home, the outside finished siding may not be in place so a length of the circuit cable should be installed and fastened inside the framed wall just inside of where the outside receptacle will be located. The cable should be secured so that it will not be damaged by insulation or sheet rock, but it must also be available so that if a cut-in box is installed you will be able to retrieve the cable and complete the installation.

Home·Electrical·Wiring

Electrical Codes for Outside Receptacles

✓	Location(s)	Category	Device(s)	Description
☐	outside	branch circuits and outlets	receptacles	A grade level receptacle is required at the front and rear of a dwelling with the maximum height of 6 1/2 feet above grade.
☐	outside balconies, decks, porches	wiring methods	receptacles	Balconies, decks, and porches that are accessible from inside the dwelling unit shall have at least one receptacle outlet installed within the perimeter. The receptacle shall not be more than 6 1/2 feet high above the surface.
☐	outside	wiring methods	receptacles	A receptacle outlet is required outdoor at the front and rear of every home. The receptacles should be not higher than 6 feet 6 inches high.
☐	outside	wiring	GFCI receptacles	An exception is a Ground Fault Protection of Equipment circuit that is dedicated to receptacles for snow-melting or deicing equipment that are not easily accessible.
☐	outside	wiring	GFCI receptacles	All 15 and 20 amp 120 volt receptacles must be GFCI protected. GFCI devices must be installed in a readily accessible location.
☐	room	wiring	GFCI receptacles	GFCI protection is NOT required receptacles located 6 feet or further from the outside edge of a wetbar sink. GFCI devices must be installed in a readily accessible location.
☐	outside	receptacles	tamper resistant	All 15 and 20 amp receptacle outlets in dwelling units must be listed tamper resistant.
☐	outside	branch circuits	receptacles	Receptacles located in a damp or wet location are required to be listed as a weather-resistant type.

Circuit Design: 120 Volt GFCI Landscape Receptacle

Example of a 120 Volt Landscape Outlet:
An exterior outlet must be located at the front and rear entrances to the home providing GFCI protection and a weatherproof cover. The circuit may be extended to provide power to other outlets and landscape lighting.

Circuit Design Table: Exterior Outlet		
Device: **GFCI Receptacle**	**GFCI Outlet Symbol**	**Application:** **Front and Rear Entrances**
	GFCI	
Circuit Size: **20 Amps, 120 Volt**	**Cable:** **#12 THWN**	**Box / Enclosure:** **1-Gang Weather Proof Box**

Wiring Notes:
When the electrical wiring is being installed in the home, the outside finished siding may not be in place so a length of the circuit cable should be installed and fastened inside the framed wall just inside of where the outside receptacle will be located. The cable should be secured so that it will not be damaged by insulation or sheet rock, but it must also be available so that if a cut-in box is installed you will be able to retrieve the cable and complete the installation.

Circuit Design: Exterior Lighting

Example of Exterior Lighting:
Exterior lighting is typically located at the front and rear entrances to the home providing adequate illumination.

Circuit Design Table: Exterior Lighting		
Device: **Exterior Lighting**	**Lighting Symbol**	**Applications:** **Exterior, Garage, Entry, Rear**
Circuit Size: **15 Amps, 120 Volt**	**Cable: Type NM** **14/2 with Ground**	**Box / Enclosure: 3-0 Inch** **Side Nail, Cut-In, Pancake**

Circuit Notes:
Exterior lighting may be required to be energy efficient compliant, and may qualify when approved lighting and or controls are installed where the lighting is operated using a manual ON light switch and auto Off device such as a built-in photo cell and motion detector.

Circuit Design: Hot Tub 240 Volt GFCI

Example of a Hot Tub Installation:
There are a few different types of hot tubs available in various sizes and with different heating types and optional devices. The specific model that is selected will provide the actual electrical circuit requirement.

Circuit Design Table: Hot Tub		
Device: 240 Volt, Hardwired	**240 Volt GFCI Symbol**	**Application:** Indoor/Outdoor
	240 GFCI	240 GFCI
Circuit Size: 240 Volt	**Cable:** 3-Wire w/ Ground	**Box / Enclosure:** Hot Tub Control Panel

Circuit Notes: All hot tubs and hydro massage tubs require a GFCI protected circuit.
Circuit Size: Consult the installation manual or the manufacturer's specifications for the specific circuit voltage and amperage.

Electrical Codes for Hot Tub

✓	Location(s)	Category	Device(s)	Description
☐	pools, spas whirlpool tubs and boathouses	GFCI	receptacle outlets	Receptacles that are within 20 feet or less of pools and outdoor hot tubs must be GFCI protected.
☐	hot tub/spa			LFMC or LFNMC is permitted up to 6 feet for a package unit hot tub or spa.
☐	hot tub/spa			A cord up to 15 feet is permitted for a GFCI-protected package unit hot tub or spa.
☐	hot tub/spa			Bands used to secure hot tub staves are exempt from bonding.
☐	pools, spas whirlpool tubs and boathouses	GFCI		GFCI protection is required for receptacles that provide power to indoor spas or hot tubs
☐	pools, spas whirlpool tubs and boathouses	GFCI		GFCI protection is required for outlets supplying power to any self-contained packaged spa, hot tub or field-assembled units with heating that is less than 50 amps.

✓	Location(s)	Category	Device(s)	Description
☐	sheds, greenhouses, pool houses, pole barns	wiring methods	receptacles	At least one receptacle outlet, in addition to those for specific equipment, shall be installed in each shed, greenhouse, pool house, pole barn, with electric power.
☐	pools, spas, whirlpool tubs and boathouses	GFCI		GFCI protection is required for all 15A and 20A receptacles located in boathouses.
☐	pools, spas, whirlpool tubs and boathouses	GFCI		GFCI protection is required for 120 volt or 240 volt boat hoists.
☐	swimming pools, fountains, permanently installed pools	GFCI	receptacle outlets	Outlets supplying pool pump motors connected to single phase, 120 volt through 240 volt branch circuits, rated for 15 or 20 amps, whether by receptacle or by direct connection, shall be provided with ground-fault circuit interrupter protection for personnel.
☐	pools, spas whirlpool tubs and boathouses	GFCI	receptacle outlets	Receptacles that are within 20 feet or less of pools and outdoor hot tubs must be GFCI protected.
☐	pools, spas whirlpool tubs and boathouses	GFCI	receptacle outlets	The distance for GFCI protection does not apply to cords that would have to pass through a window or a door.
☐	pools, spas whirlpool tubs and boathouses	GFCI	receptacle outlets	Existing luminaires are allowed to be less than 5 feet horizontal if greater than 5 feet vertical above the water and they are GFCI protected.

Electrical Codes for Pool Pg-2

✓	Location(s)	Category	Device(s)	Description
☐	pools, spas whirlpool tubs and boathouses	GFCI	receptacle outlets	GFCI protection is required for luminaires and lighting outlets that are less than 10 feet horizontally from an outdoor pool or spa edge unless greater than 5 feet vertically above the water.
☐	swimming pools, fountains, permanently installed pools	GFCI	lighting luminaries	A ground-fault circuit interrupter shall be installed in the branch circuit supplying luminaries operating at more than the low-voltage contact limit such as there is no shock hazard during relamping.
☐	swimming pools, fountains, permanently installed pools	GFCI	LED lighting luminaries	Where the luminaire operates over the low-voltage contact limit, a flush deck junction box shall be 4 feet from the edge of the pool. Class 2 circuit.
☐	swimming pools, fountains, permanently installed pools	equipotential bonding grounding	bonded parts of pool fixed metal parts	All fixed metal parts shall be bonded including, but not limited to, metal piping, metal awnings, metal fences, and metal door and window frames.
☐	swimming pools, fountains, permanently installed pools	equipotential bonding grounding	bonded parts of pool construction	A copper conductor grid shall be provided and conform to the contour of the pool. The perimeter surface shall extend for 3 feet horizontally beyond the inside walls of the pool and shall include unpaved surfaces, as well as poured concrete surfaces and other types of paving.

Electrical Codes for Pool Pg-3

✓	Location(s)	Category	Device(s)	Description
☐	pools, spas whirlpool tubs and boathouses	GFCI		GFCI protection is required for a pool cover motor and controller.
☐	pools, spas whirlpool tubs and boathouses	GFCI		GFCI protection is required for receptacles that are located 10 feet or less of indoor spas or tubs.
☐	pools, spas whirlpool tubs and boathouses	GFCI		GFCI protection is required for receptacles that provide power to indoor spas or hot tubs.
☐	pools, spas whirlpool tubs and boathouses	GFCI		GFCI protection is not required for outlets supplying listed units with integral GFCI protection.
☐	pools, spas whirlpool tubs and boathouses	GFCI		GFCI protection is required for outlets supplying power to any self-contained packaged spa, hot tub or field-assembled units with heating that is less than 50 amps.
☐		overhead service drop clearances	overhead conductor clearance	Any direction within swimming pool water must be 22 1/2 ft.

Circuit Design: 240 Volt EV Charging Station

Example of an EV Charger Installation:
Electric Vehicle Charging Stations will soon be installed in most new homes. Some EV Charging Stations require a circuit similar to that of a dryer or range circuit.

Circuit Design Table: EV Charging Station		
Device: **Control Panel** **240 Volt, Hardwired**	**240 Volt Outlet Symbol**	**Application:** **Garage**
	240 Volt	240
Circuit Size: **240 Volt GFCI**	**Cable:** **2-Wire w/ Ground**	**Connection:** **Plug compatible for the E.V.**

Circuit Notes: The specific circuit voltage and amperage for the charging station will depend on the EV that will be connected. Some EV's will charge from 120 or 240 volt chargers, 240 volt would charge faster than 120 volt.

Circuit Size: Consult the EV charging station manufacturer's specifications for the specific circuit voltage and amperage.

Electrical Codes for EV Charger

✓	Location(s)	Category	Device(s)	Description
☐		EV charging	electric vehicle charging systems	EV charging systems greater than 20 amps must not have exposed live parts.
☐		EV charging	electric vehicle charging systems	An EV coupler must be listed and labeled for EV.
☐		EV charging	electric vehicle charging systems	The EV charger Interlock must de-energize the connector when uncoupled from the EV.
☐		EV charging	electric vehicle charging systems	An Electric Vehicle is permitted as a standby power source through a listed utility interactive connection.

Circuit Design: 220 Volt Well Pump

Example of a Well Pump Circuit:
Well pump circuits are typically 220/240 volt. The location of the well may be close to the home or a long distance away. When long cable runs will be required it will be necessary to adjust the wire size for voltage drop.

Circuit Design Table: Well Pump		
Device: 240 Volt, Hardwired	**240 Volt Symbol**	**Application:** Exterior
	220 Volt	PRESSURE TANK
Circuit Size: 220/240 Volt	**Conduit:** PVC Sch40-THWN	**Box / Enclosure:** Well Pump Disconnect

Circuit Notes: The size of the well pump circuit will depend on the exact pump and horse power that is to be installed.

Considerations: The depth of the well will be factored in by the well drilling company for sizing the pump which will also be used to determine the size of the cable. The climate of the location should be considered when deciding the well pump circuit. In freezing conditions where there may be a pump house it may be helpful to install a 120/240 Volt sub-panel that is large enough to supply power to the well pump circuit and one or two 120 volt circuits for a light fixture and freeze cable or tape.

Circuit Design: Septic System 120 Volt

Example of a Septic System Circuit:
Septic systems will require a dedicated circuit which will be used for the alarm and control system if a pump is used.

Circuit Design Table: Septic System		
Device: Septic Control System	**120 Volt Symbol**	**Application: Exterior Septic Tank Location**
Circuit Size: 20 Amps, 120 Volt	**Cable: Romex 12/2 with Ground**	**Box / Enclosure: Septic Control System**

Wiring Notes: New septic systems in most areas require either one or two separate 20 amp circuits. The number of circuits will depend on the control panel that will be installed. If one circuit is required then the control panel will share the circuit between two circuit breakers, one for the pump motor and one for the control system and alarm.

Dial Up Phone Cable: In many areas a phone cable will be required as well. This will allow the septic control system to be monitored by an off site monitoring dispatch service.

Circuit Design: Snow Melt 240 Volt GFCI

Example of a Snow or Ice Melt System Circuit:
Snow and ice melting systems are custom designed for each application. Snow melting systems are great for keeping snow and ice from accumulating on walkway, stairway and driveway areas.

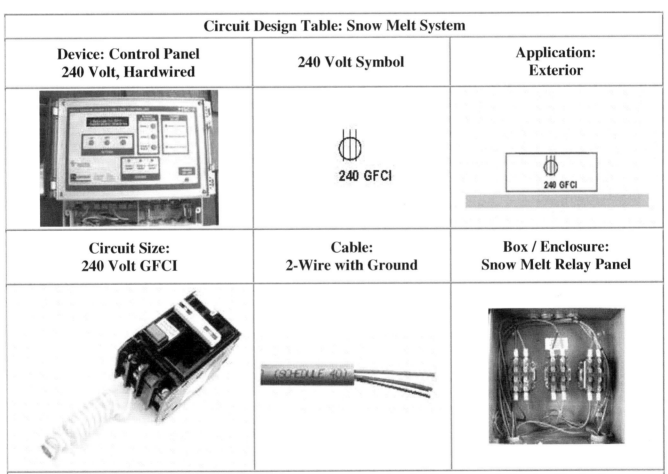

Circuit Design Table: Snow Melt System		
Device: Control Panel 240 Volt, Hardwired	**240 Volt Symbol**	**Application: Exterior**
	240 GFCI	240 GFCI
Circuit Size: 240 Volt GFCI	**Cable:** 2-Wire with Ground	**Box / Enclosure:** Snow Melt Relay Panel

Circuit Notes: All electric snow and ice melting systems require GFCI protected circuits. Typically residential systems work best with 240 volt heat material.

Circuit Size: Consult the manufacturer's specifications for the specific number of circuits and the amperage.

Electrical Codes for Snow & Ice Melting

✓	Location(s)	Category	Device(s)	Description
☐	outside	wiring	GFCI receptacles	An exception is a Ground Fault Protection of Equipment circuit that is dedicated to receptacles for snow-melting or deicing equipment that are not easily accessible.
☐	outside	deicing snow melt heating cables	GFCI	GFCI Ground fault circuit interrupter protection of equipment shall be provided for fixed outdoor electric deicing and snow-melting equipment.

Lighting

LIGHTING FIXTURES

INTERIOR

Wiring Method: Ceiling Fans

Options for the Ceiling Fan that Determine the Wiring Methods

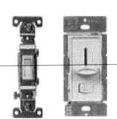

Switch and Control Options - Single Switches or 3-Way, Fan Speed Control, Light Switch or Dimmer, or Remote Control

- The type of controls for the ceiling fan and light will determine the type of cable and the size of the of the switch box. If separate switches will be installed then a 3-wire cable will be required. If in doubt, wire for two switches with a 3-wire cable.

Box Type, Mounting and Wiring Decisions

- Identify the construction and framing methods to determine the type of boxes that will be installed. It is best to bring the power into the switch box; especially if a shallow ceiling fan box will be installed. Use only rated boxes for ceiling fans.

Installing Boxes Rated for Ceiling Fans

- Approved boxes rated for ceiling fans must be selected and installed onto a well supported structure. Many different types of rated boxes are available for various structural configurations.

Installing the Ceiling Fan

- Care should be taken to use dependable mounting hardware and screws for a firm installation that will prevent movement that can cause the fan to wobble.

Installing Switches and Controls

- There are several options for controlling a ceiling fan, from basic wall switches which require hardwiring to fully programmable handheld remote controls that only require a power source.

Wiring Diagram: Ceiling Fan and Switch

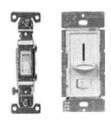

Switch Wiring Options for Ceiling Fans

There may be either one or two wall switches installed to control the ceiling fan and light.

The power source is located at the switch box.

This diagram shows the power entering into the circuit at the switch box location, and then sending power through the switch up to the ceiling fan. For one switch control a 2-wire cable is required; two switches require a 3-wire cable.

One switch controls fan, one switch controls the light.

One switch controls both the fan and light.

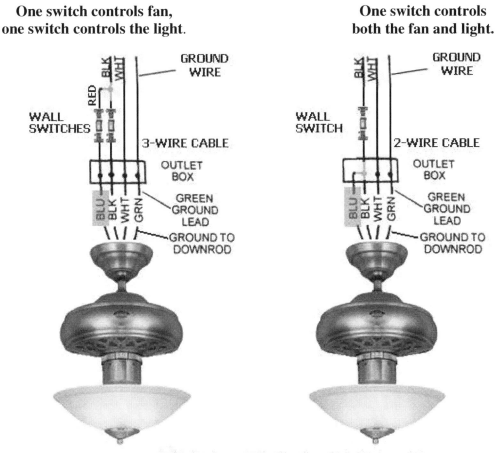

Adjustment for the Blue Light Fixture Wire

Note typical for all cables: A dimmer switch may be used for compatible light fixtures.
2-wire cables and 3-wire cables are with a ground wire and are sized for the circuit rating.

Wiring Diagram: Ceiling Fan and Remote Control

Ceiling Fan Remote Controls

Many ceiling fans now come with built in remote controls, however remote control module kits may be purchased and added to most ceiling fans without the remote capability.

The Advantages of a Remote Control for a Ceiling Fan

As shown below, the only requirement for the basic remote control module is power at the ceiling junction box of the ceiling fan. Once the remote module has been installed a remote control may adjust the fan speed and level of lighting. If a wall switch is installed it will act as the master control because the wall switch will controls the power to the ceiling fan remote module.

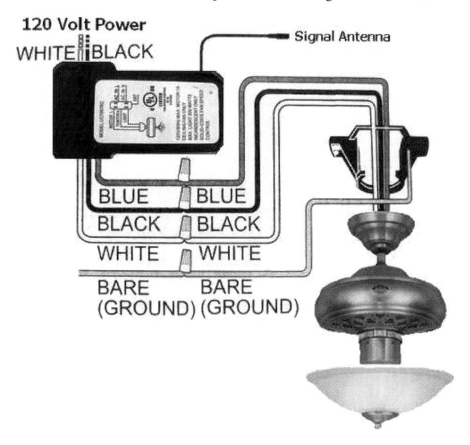

Note: Pull chains on the ceiling fan should be in the full ON position, otherwise the remote control module will not be able to control the fan to the fullest extent.

Installing Fluorescent Light Fixtures Pg-1

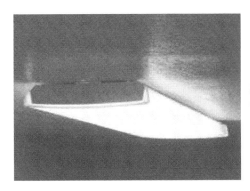

Surface mounted fluorescent light fixtures are great for the garage, workshop and laundry room.

Uncrate the light fixture, remove the center ballast cover and inspect all the parts.

If you are installing more than one light fixture then you may wish to locate all of the lenses and cover plates separately or near the areas where the light fixtures will be installed.

The light fixture will be equipped with a 1/2 inch knock-out that can be used to bring the electrical wires from the ceiling box into the fixture.

From the center knock-out, measure the distance to the mounting holes at each end of the fixture.

Measure out the ceiling area for the light fixture, using nearby walls as a reference point, to the center of the ceiling light fixture box. Transfer this measurement out to each end of the light fixture as noted from the light fixture.
Scan the ceiling with a stud finder looking for obstacles or framing material. If the area is clear and hollow then toggle bolts may be used, otherwise wood screws and washers may be used where there is framing support.

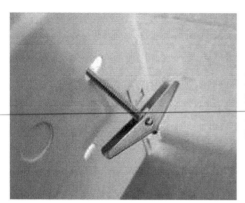

Insert the toggle bolts at the appropriate locations of the light fixture.

Remove the knock-out and install an insulated bushing and prepare the ceiling wire to be inserted through the fixture bushing.

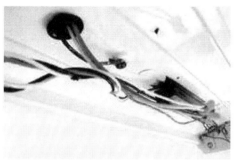

Carefully guide the wires from the ceiling box into the light fixture, then insert the toggle bolts and/or install the wood screws.

Measure off of the side of the fixture to the wall and adjust the fixture as needed.

Make the wiring connections and attach the ground wire to the ground screw of the light fixture.

Install the lamps so that both pins are inside each socket at both ends and then gently twist each lamp about 45 degrees, you should see the alignment mark on the base of the lamp lined up with the opening of each socket.

Install the fixture lens on one side of the fixture, and then hinge it closed to the other side and adjust the lens until if is properly seated in the provided channel.

Upgrading Fluorescent Light Fixtures from: Magnetic T12 Ballast to: Electronic T8 Ballast

Advantages: No flicker when cold and saves energy. Convert your existing light fixture.

Most 4-foot florescent light fixtures may be upgraded simply by replacing the old magnetic ballast with a new solid state electronic ballast, and LED conversions will be possible as well.

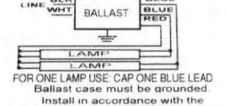

Match the new replacement electronic ballast with the old ballast.
Must be the stated Voltage.
Must be for the same length and number of lamps.

Turn OFF the power source to the light fixture.
Cut the wires close to the old ballast.
Cap the black and white wires of the power source.
CAUTION: The old ballast may be hot, if so then let it cool down before replacing.

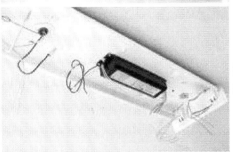

Support the old ballast and remove the nut that holds it into place, and then remove the ballast.

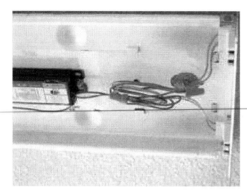

Install the new electronic ballast and make the new wiring connections as shown on the wiring diagram of the new ballast.

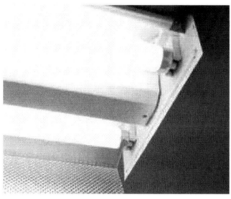

The old T12 Lamps are to be replaced with new T8 lamps, be sure to select the right calvin or color.

Swag Chain Light Fixtures Pg-1

Swag lighting is great for displaying a custom decorative light fixture, or for adding light to a dark area without installing new wiring.

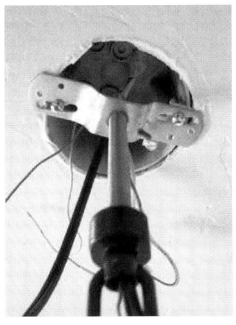

An existing light fixture box provides the power for this ceiling swag fixture; however the fixture cord and chain may be run to a wall outlet as well.

An adapter bracket and 3/8 inch all-thread pipe is installed to support the fixture canopy which also allows the fixture cord to enter the electrical junction box.

The mounting hardware must all be measured and organized to enable the finished assembly.

Care must be taken to make sure the fixture cord and ground wire is not too tight so the weight of the light fixture will be on the swag chain and not the wiring.

Swag Chain Light Fixtures Pg-2

A ground wire should be installed and bonded to the metal parts of the light fixture and travel with the power cord through the swag chain.

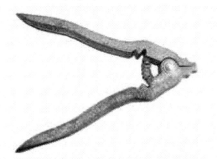

This pair of chain pliers is the sure way for adjusting the fixture chain without scratching or damaging the appearance.

The end of the chain pliers is used to open the fixture chain links and has two positions to help with larger chains.

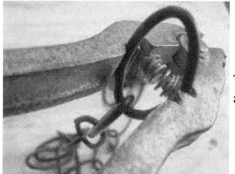

The inner handle area of the chain pliers has two set of notches which allow closing the chain links once the exact length is determined.

Tip: A wooden dowel is helpful to organize long lengths of fixture chain and will allow inserting the fixture cord through several sections at one time.

Make Your Own Light Fixtures Pg-1

Use your imagination to create just about any kind of light fixture with the right fixture parts and some safety precautions.

Lamp kits may be purchased at most hardware stores to help create any light fixture with a single light bulb.

Lamp sockets are available with a few to choose from depending on the light fixture:
No switch, the fixture controlled by an external switch, an ON-OFF push switch, a rotary ON-OFF switch, or a rotary switch for the three-way light bulbs.

Make Your Own Light Fixtures Pg-2

A lamp shade support hoop may be installed by adding the hoop bracket which is added just below the lamp base during the parts assembly.

The base section of the light fixture can be just about anything you wish as long as it will be safe.

Many lamp kits come with a pre-wired length of light fixture cord complete with the plug.

Note: Lamp kits are typically rated for a maximum size light bulb. Care must be taken to prevent hot light bulbs from coming too close or into contact with combustible materials of the light fixture and the surface areas where installed.

Telephone and Communication

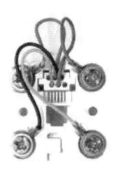

TELCOM
Data and Communications

Telephone and Data Communications

Internet Data Application - DSL - Digital Subscriber Line

Cat 5e or Cat 6

**4 Pair Cable
22 or 24 gauge**

**RJ45 Male Connector
for Cat 5e or Cat 6**

Data / DSL Internet

**RJ45 Modular Jack
for Cat 5e or Cat 6**

Data / DSL Internet

Internal Computer Networking

**Single Computer
DSL Hub**

**Single Port
DSL Network Hub**
may connect to one computer or a network

**Hardwired
Network Router**

**4-Port Network Router
Firewall and
IP Configurations**

**Wireless
Network Router**

**4-Port Network Router
Firewall and
IP Configurations**

**Car 5e or Cat 6 Patch
Cable**

**Connection from Router to Desktop
Computer**

Home·Electrical·Wiring

Circuit Design: Data - DSL Internet Service

Example of a DSL Data Service:
In most areas an internet connection is available through the local telephone company who may provide DSL service using the existing telephone line or by installing a new or additional DSL line to the home.

Circuit Design Table: DSL Data Service		
Device: Data Jack to DSL Router	**Data Symbol**	**Application:** Various Locations
	▼	
Service: TelCo Utility Company	**Cable:** Cat 5 or Cat 5e	**Box / Enclosure:** 1-Gang Face nail frame

Circuit Notes: The incoming DSL service is typically located at the same location as the external telephone equipment which is located near the main electrical panel. The telephone company typically provides a DSL connection box or integrates the DSL service into the existing telephone box. The internal home telephone cables must be rated for data such as Cat5 or Cat5e which are installed from this location and out to one or more telephone jacks. For a single line DSL service, one phone line may be installed from the TelCo/DSL box to the Phone/Data location in the home.

Internet Service - DSL / Cable Modem

Internet Service: This diagram below shows the typical cable connections for internet service. The Stand Alone Gateway Modem or Router type and port labels may vary depending on the actual type of internet service and modem or router.

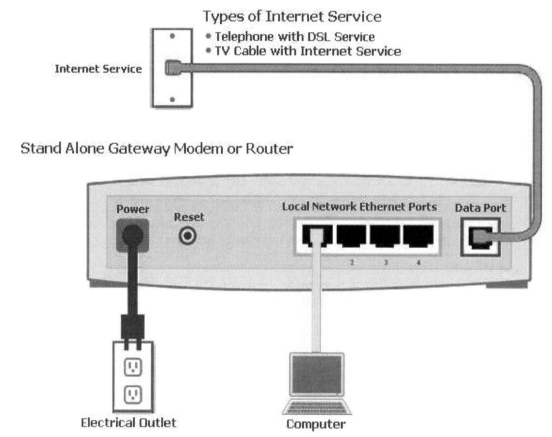

Types of Internet Service
- Telephone with DSL Service
- TV Cable with Internet Service

Internet Service

Stand Alone Gateway Modem or Router

Power   Reset   Local Network Ethernet Ports   Data Port

Electrical Outlet   Computer

Connect one end of the Data Cable to the internet service wall jack.
Connect the other end of the Data Cable to the Data Port on the Gateway Router.

Connect the Local Network Cable into one of the Local Network Ports of the Gateway Router.
Connect the other end of the Local Network Cable into the Data Port of the Computer.

Connect the Gateway Router Power Adapter to the Power Port on the Gateway Router.
Plug in the Power Adapter to the Electrical Outlet.

Data Com Wiring

Data Com Wiring for Internet and Home Network

Wiring Data Com
Data Com Network Wiring

SAFETY INSTRUCTIONS
1. Never install data com wiring during a lightning storm.
2. Never install data com jacks in a wet location unless the jack is specifically designed for use in wet locations.
3. Never touch uninsulated data com wires or terminals unless the telephone line has been disconnected at the network interface.
4. Use caution when installing or modifying data com cables.

IMPORTANT INSTRUCTIONS
When using your data com equipment, basic precautions should always be followed to reduce the risk of fire, electric shock, and injury to persons including the following:
1. Read and understand all instructions.
2. Follow all warnings and instructions marked on the telephone equipment.
3. Do not use telephone equipment near water, such as a tub, bathroom sink, kitchen sink or laundry tub, in a wet basement, or near a swimming pool.
4. Never push objects of any kind into data com equipment or data com connection slots as they may touch dangerous voltages.

Telephone Service

Telephone Service Terminal Enclosure

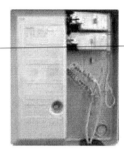

Telephone Wiring Components

	Cat 3	**3 Pair Cable** **22 or 24 gauge**
	Cat 5e	**4 Pair Cable** **22 or 24 gauge**
	RJ11 Male Connector **for Cat 3 or Cat 5e**	**Telephone Service**
	RJ11 6-Pin **Phone Outlet**	**Standard Telephone** **Wall Jack**
	Scotch 3M UL Splice, **with corrosion inhibitor**	**Splice for telephone wires, 22 or** **24 gauge.** **Insert wires and compress the** **connector.**

Note: The standard telephone system only requires 1 pair of 2-wires for a telephone to work (also known as Tip and Ring). The extra wires of the telephone cable may be used for additional service lines or spares.

Circuit Design: Telephone

Example of a Home Telephone System:
With the changes in technology and communications we see a growing number of wireless communication devices being used. Perhaps one day the need for communications cable will not be necessary, however until that time we will continue to install high grade communications cable for the default telephone services.

Circuit Design Table: Telephone System		
Device: Telephone Jack or Connector	**Telephone Symbol**	**Application:** Various Telephone Locations
	▼	
Service: TelCo Utility Company	**Cable:** Cat 3 or Cat 5	**Box / Enclosure:** 1-Gang Face nail frame
Circuit Notes: The incoming telephone service is typically located at the same location as the main electrical panel. The telephone company typically provides the main connection box. The internal home telephone cables are installed from this location and out to each telephone jack. For a single line service, one phone line may be installed from the TelCo box and daisy chained through each phone location in the home.		

Wiring Diagram: Telephone Jack

Telephone Wiring Explanations for:
6-Wire Cat 5 and 8-Wire Cat 6
4-Wire Cat 3

WIRE COLOR CODES

Standard 4-Pair Wiring Color Codes		
PAIR 1	T	White/Blue
	R	Blue/White
PAIR 2	T	White/Orange
	R	Orange/White
PAIR 3	T	White/Green
	R	Green/White
PAIR 4	T	White/Brown
	R	Brown/White

Note: For 6-wire jacks use pair 1, 2 and 3 color codes.
For 4-wire jacks use pair 1 and 2 color codes.

A. Band-Striped Twisted-Pair Wire

B. Solid-Color Twisted-Pair Wire

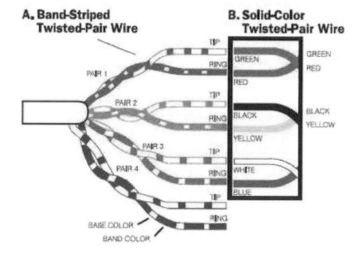

C. Quad Wire*
(Solid-Color, Non-Twisted Wire)

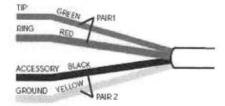

Wiring a Telephone Jack Pg-1

Telephone Jack Wiring

Pre Wire Phone Jacks
Most wall phone jacks come configured for a 2-line cord even thought a 1-line phone will work just fine. You are probably wondering why the extra pairs? Well, they will be used if you ever decide to add another phone line or if for some reason the primary pair stops working, then one of the spare pairs can be used.

Two Lines from one Telephone Jack
This style of phone jack can be pre-wired for a 2-line phone service, giving you the opportunity to have a second phone number that can be used for a business line or a fax machine.

SAFETY INSTRUCTIONS
1. Never install telephone wiring during a lightning storm.
2. Never install telephone jacks in a wet location unless the jack is specifically designed for use in wet locations.
3. Never touch uninsulated telephone wires or terminals unless the telephone line has been disconnected at the network interface.
4. Use caution when installing or modifying telephone lines.

IMPORTANT INSTRUCTIONS
When using your telephone equipment, basic precautions should always be followed to reduce the risk of fire, electric shock and injury to persons, including the following:
1. Read and understand all instructions.
2. Follow all warnings and instructions marked on the telephone equipment.
3. Do not use telephone equipment near water, such as a tub, bathroom sink, kitchen sink or laundry tub, in a wet basement, or near a swimming pool.
4. Never push objects of any kind into telephone equipment or telephone connection slots as they may touch dangerous voltages.

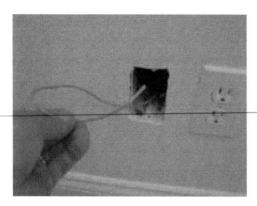

Remove the outer jacket of the telephone cable using a larger wire gauge for the wire strippers.

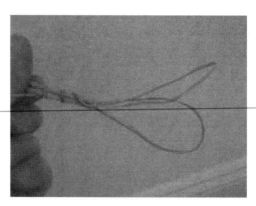

Only two wires are needed for each phone line, but four wires may be attached to the phone jack. The extra pairs may be wrapped onto the cable.

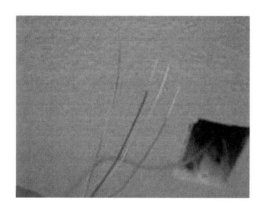

Strip off the insulation from the wire pairs.

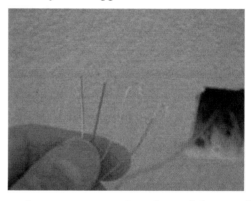

Create a loop to prepare the wires of the terminals.

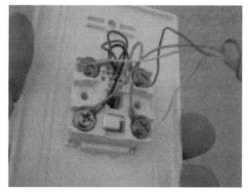

Make sure the wires are well under the screw terminals.

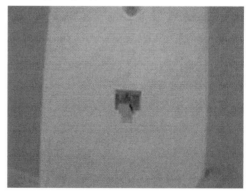

Mount the phone jack and your ready for service.

CCTV - TV Cable Service

CCTV Service Terminal Enclosure and Cables

Single RG6 Cable

**Primary TV
RJ6 Coax Cable**

Dual RG6 Cable

**Satellite Dish CCTV
2nd RJ6 Coax Cable**

CCTV Cable Accessories

**RG6 HI-Def
F-Connector**

**Connection to the TV Jack or
the TV Receiver Equipment**

TV Coax Splitter

TV Cable Distribution

TV Jack

Notes: If a home mounted dish or TV network system will be mounted at the home then a cable set may be required to be installed from the dish location to the main CCTV Enclosure. Some CCTV services may require a telephone jack to be installed at the TV Receiver location.

Electrical Codes for CATV & Telephone

✓	Location(s)	Category	Device(s)	Description
☐	feeders and services	overhead services		Only power cables are allowed to be attached to service mast. (No cable or phone drops allowed.)
☐	service grounding	grounding electrode conductors	TV and telephone	An intersystem bonding termination for connecting intersystem bonding conductors required for other systems shall be provided external to enclosures at the service equipment or metering equipment enclosure at the disconnecting means for any additional building or structure and be accessible for connection and inspection, consist of a set of terminals, not interfere with opening the enclosure, located at the service equipment, at the disconnecting means, and the terminals shall be listed as grounding and bonding equipment.
☐	service panel grounding	grounding electrode conductors	grounding	Some portion of grounding electrode conductor must be accessible at service for grounding of other systems. (Telephone or Cable TV)
☐	wiring	wiring methods	strapping	Used to secure NM, Coax, Telephone Cables to framing members, NM, Coax, Telephone.
☐	bonding	intersystem bonding		A minimum 6 AWG Cu bond must connect to CATV or phone electrodes.

Home Entertainment System

Multimedia Panel

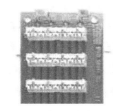

**Cat 3 - 3 Twisted Pairs
and RJ11 Connector**

**RJ6 Coax Cable
F-Connector**

**Cat 5 - 4 Twisted Pairs
and RJ11 Connector**

Audio Cables

14-2 with Jacket

14-2 Flat Cable

Upgrades and Rewiring

UPGRADE and RE-WIRING

Electrical System Inspection and Evaluation

This checklist will help to evaluate the existing electrical system to determine where improvements could be made, starting with smoke detectors and ground fault and arc fault protection.

Smoke Detectors

☐ Smoke Detectors: Bedrooms, Hallways, Stairs, Occupied Rooms.

GFCI, AFCI and Receptacle Outlets

☐ GFCI Outlets or Circuits: Bathroom, Kitchen, Laundry, Garage, Outdoor

☐ AFCI Outlets or Circuits: Bedrooms and Enforced Areas

☐ Grounded Circuits: Receptacles throughout the Home

Lighting

☐ Closet Lighting Fixture Type and Proximity Spacing

☐ Outdated Fixtures or Oversized Light Bulbs

☐ Fixtures at Entrance Areas, Walkways and Driveway

Existing Circuit Problems

☐ Tripping Circuit Breakers or Blowing Fuses

☐ Extension Cords being Used

☐ Need for New Electric Appliances or Equipment

Age or Condition of Electrical Wiring

☐ Knob and Tube Wiring

☐ Presence of Cloth Insulated Cable or Wiring

☐ Unsafe or Illegal Electrical Wiring

Main Service Panel Capacity and Circuit Sizing

☐ Amperage and Space Capacity for Circuits

☐ Bonded Ground System

☐ Proper Rated Circuit Protection for the Circuit Wire Type and Size

☐ Circuit Labeling and Identification Directory

Troubleshooting

TROUBLESHOOTING

The Most Common Electrical Problems

Did you plan your project first?
My answers for many project questions starts out with "have you planned out the loads you intend to be adding?" Begin by calculating the load of your project to determine the size of the circuit or additional panel. If the distance is greater than 100 feet then determine the voltage drop factors. Plan your project carefully and submit the plan to your local building department and obtain a permit.

Check your circuit breakers and GFCI's first.
Even more of my answers begin with "Identify the affected circuit and check the circuit breakers and test the GFI's". Many times a circuit may have tripped off and the circuit breaker just needs to be reset.

Never replace a fuse or circuit breaker with a larger one. NEVER!
Fuses and circuit breakers are sized according to wire gauge and the type of insulation. If you increase to a larger size you will be endangering your family and your home which could very possibly start on fire. If a fuse blows or a circuit breaker trips off it is doing its job of protecting the circuit wiring and components. Conditions such as these are due to an overloaded circuit or a problem within the circuit which will require a qualified electrician to identify and repair the problem.

The age of the home and electrical wiring.
Sooner or later, an older home will require the electrical panel and circuits to be inspected. Often it will be determined that the home needs to be brought up to the current electrical codes, and the electrical service should be increased. If this is the case then don't put it off. At least start with the safety items first such as installing smoke detectors, GFCI outlets and AFCI circuit breakers. These three items are among the most important items to protect you and your family against potential electrical hazards.

Often a circuit has a serious problem and requires a professional.
Electricity flowing through wired circuits and devices produces heat which causes expansion and contraction of the circuit components. This can lead to loose and deteriorated connections which can produce a short circuit or burnt circuit components. Visual inspections and electrical measurements will help pinpoint the trouble so the necessary repairs may be applied to return the normal service.

Unfortunately, problems may occur when hiring an unqualified electrician.
If you hired an inexperienced or unqualified person to save money and expected a professional job then shame on you, you deserve what you get! The only way to avoid this all too common problem is to do the job right, plan the job thoroughly, hire qualified licensed people, file a permit, have all the inspections, and then pay the bill in full.

Seek professional help from a licensed electrician.
Hire only certified or licensed electrical contractors to perform your electrical wiring or to troubleshoot serious circuit problems and make the necessary repairs. If you do not heed this advice, you're asking for trouble.

Troubleshooting Electrical Problems Pg-1

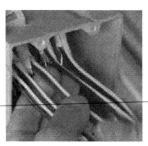

I must admit that my dad loved troubleshooting! He would rather take on the task of troubleshooting electrical wiring then he would construction jobs, and Yes - My dad was the <u>best troubleshooter</u> there was; and I'm glad to say that I listened and paid attention to his teachings about troubleshooting. Many times it pays to be quiet and just observe.

Ask questions - then Listen, and the pieces to the puzzle start to appear.

Quick Checks just to make sure:
Is the switch "ON"?
Is the light bulb burned out?
Is a GFI receptacle or GFCI breaker tripped?
Is a circuit breaker tripped or a fuse blown - If so find out why!

Sometimes troubleshooting is easy and extremely obvious - like a switch that was forgotten about, or yes - the darn light bulb was just burnt out. You may even discover that a GFCI receptacle or breaker was tripped. There have been times when the tripped GFCI plug was behind a pile of boxes in the garage and no one ever knew there was a plug there. Well, I could go on and on with stories about troubleshooting electrical wiring, but lets get to a method that could save you a lot of time, frustration and a bunch of money.

The method I've learned is an easy one, and you've probably already used it several times on other applications, here it is:

The Process of Elimination Which Starts With Identification

<u>Safety First</u>
Be sure <u>not</u> to work with energized wires or circuits.
Identify the circuit, shut it off, and then tag the circuit to keep it off.
Before testing, make sure to cap your wires with wire nuts or insulate them with electrical tape when you need to turn the circuit back on.

Identify the HOT wire coming in with red or black electrical tape so you can identify this wire from all the others. This is what I call "flagging the hot wire".

Troubleshooting Electrical Problems Pg-2

Very Important: If you don't feel comfortable working on your electrical problem, please don't take chances - call a professional electrician.

Here is the process
Make sure to identify which cable provides the power coming in.
Do not work on the circuit with the power on. Turn the power off and label the circuit so others know you are working on it.

Positively identify all the cables - What cable goes where.
Check all devices served by each cable. Disconnect any devices that may be connected to any associated cable. Check these devices to see if they are malfunctioning. Isolate or remove any device in order to eliminate a failing component.

Is a switch involved? - Check the switch with an OHM Meter.
Is it a fixture that doesn't work? Safely test the fixture with a spare cord to see if it works. If it does not - check the fixture wiring, bulbs etc.

Neutral Wires
Sometimes a HOT wire will test ok to path to ground typically a ground wire, but will not test ok to the white neutral wire. This can be caused by a few things, most of all a loose or burnt connection that has burnt clear of the connection point such as a screw on a receptacle or the insertion point on the back of a receptacle. Without the neutral a device will not work. Be sure to check all the neutral connections at the source and at any junction leading to the problem area.

A Warning about Space Heaters:
Some high wattage space heaters used over a period of time can cause a receptacle to become over heated, especially on the neutral side.

If a receptacle becomes discolored where the cord is plugged in then chances are the wiring attached to the receptacle inside the receptacle box will have experienced over heating and could possibly be burnt. Make sure these receptacle circuits are turned off before removing the cover plate and receptacle for inspection.

Checking The Wire Connections
Make sure your connections are well made. A loose connection will also cause shorts and create burnt wires which could result in a potential fire hazard.

Twist wires together using pliers before screwing on any wire nuts, this ensures a good connection. Don't over tighten wire nuts, but make sure they are on tight.

As the circuit and all the components are checked you should identify the problem. Most of the time it is something very obvious.

Troubleshooting: Tripping Circuits

 Circuit breakers function as Over Current Protection devices, and an over current condition may be caused by several events which may be a wiring problem or an equipment problem.

Tripping Circuit Breaker

- If the circuit breaker is tripping OFF then this may be an indication of a direct short which would be caused by not having the circuit wiring connections configured correctly.
- Identifying the wiring will help determine the correct wiring connections.
- The circuit wiring should be verified using a voltage tester or an OHM Meter.

How to Determine the Cause of a Tripping Circuit Breaker

A circuit breaker may trip due to a direct short condition caused by:

✓	A hot wire connected to a ground wire or grounded source.
✓	A hot wire connected to a neutral wire.
✓	Two separate circuits connected together.
✓	A fault within the electrical circuit or the device being connected.

Other factors that may cause a circuit breaker to trip:

✓	An overloaded circuit.
✓	Faulty equipment.
✓	A defective circuit breaker.

Troubleshooting: Lost Circuit Power

Identifying the Cause of Electrical Circuit Loss

The Problem:

Circuits in the home will go off but the circuit breaker does not trip off. It's as if there was a loss of power.

Checks to Make:

Identify Circuit Loss Factors

- When the circuit is interrupted, is there a loss of both the hot and the neutral?
- Do the circuits stop working at certain times of the day?
- Is there a pattern that can be identified with the loss of power?
- Is there other electrical equipment that is related to this pattern?
- When the circuit restores power, does this event have a pattern as well?
- Are there any automated controls in the home for items such as the water heater, hot tub or similar equipment?
- Has the circuit wiring been identified and are there any junction boxes, if so have they been inspected?

Recommended:

Inspections and Repairs

- Locate and inspect any devices or integrated circuit components related to this power loss.
- Abnormal damaged or burnt wiring connections will need to be repaired as needed.

How to Solve Window Air Conditioner Electrical Problems

Window Air Conditioners and Electrical Circuits

The Problem:

A window air conditioner was purchased and plugged into an existing outlet circuit of a room. The outlet circuit is a branch circuit and is rated at 15 amps. There are existing devices plugged into the circuit. The home is an older home. The additional load of the air conditioner that was added to the existing circuit helped to accelerate a deteriorating splice condition to the point of circuit failure at a splice joint.

The Solution:

Locate and Repair the Electrical Short

- The addition of the window air conditioner plugged into an existing shared circuit has caused an electrical short somewhere within the circuit wiring, most likely at an outlet or a splice in one of the outlets of the shared circuit.
- The faulty splice point will need to be located and repaired. The fault may be found at the attachment of the wiring to the outlet which will require the outlet to be replaced.

Recommended:

Install a Dedicated Circuit for the Air Conditioner

- It is best to install a dedicated circuit for window air conditioning units because they typically require a high amount of power.

Glossary

GLOSSARY

Electrical Code Terminology Pg-1

ACCESSIBLE: (As applied to equipment) Admitting close approach: not guarded by locked doors, elevation or other effective means.

ACCESSIBLE: (As applied to wiring methods) Capable of being removed or exposed without damaging the building.

ACCESSIBLE, READILY: (Readily accessible) Capable of being reached quickly for operation, renewal, or inspections, without requiring those to whom ready access is requisite to climb over or remove obstacles or to resort to portable ladders, chairs, etc.

Code Adoption Information: The codes shown are examples only and may not be current or accurate for your application or jurisdiction. Contact your local building authority for complete information.

AMPACITY: The current in amperes a conductor can carry continuously under the conditions of use without exceeding its temperature rating.

APPLIANCE: An appliance is utilization equipment, generally other than industrial, normally built in standardized sizes or types, which is installed or connected as a unit to perform one or more functions such as clothes washing, air conditioning, food mixing, deep frying, etc.

APPROVED: Acceptable to the authority having jurisdiction. The phrase authority having jurisdiction is used in NFPA documents in a broad manner since jurisdictions and "approval" agencies vary, as do their responsibilities. Where public safety is primary, the authority having jurisdiction may be a federal, state, local, or other regional department or individual such as a fire chief, fire marshal, chief of a fire prevention bureau, labor department, health department, building official, electrical inspector, or others having statutory authority. For insurance purposes, an insurance inspection department, rating bureau, or other insurance company representative may be the authority having jurisdiction. In many circumstances the property owner or the owner's designated agent assumes the role of the authority having jurisdiction; at government installations, the commanding officer or departmental official may be the authority having jurisdiction.

AUTOMATIC: Self-acting, operating by its own mechanism when actuated by some impersonal influence, as for example, a change in current , pressure, temperature, or mechanical configuration.

BRANCH CIRCUIT: The circuit conductors between the final over current device protecting the circuit and the outlet(s).

BRANCH CIRCUIT, APPLIANCE: A branch circuit supplying energy to one or more outlets to which appliances are to be connected; such circuits to have no permanently connected lighting fixtures not a part of an appliance. Appliance branch circuits for a kitchen, pantry, etc. and for laundry areas are not permitted to have any other outlets or permanently connected lighting fixtures connected to them.

BRANCH CIRCUIT, GENERAL PURPOSE: A branch circuit that supplies two or more receptacles or outlets for lighting and appliances.

Electrical Code Terminology Pg-2

BRANCH CIRCUIT, INDIVIDUAL: A branch circuit that supplies only one utilization equipment. An individual branch circuit shall be permitted to supply any load for which it is rated: for example, one range, or one space heater, or one motor. A branch circuit may be installed to supply one duplex receptacle, which can accommodate two cord-connected and plug-connected appliances or similar equipment. This circuit would not be considered an individual branch circuit.

BRANCH CIRCUIT, MULTIWIRE: A branch circuit that consists of two or more ungrounded conductors that have a voltage between them and a grounded conductor that has equal voltage between it and each ungrounded conductor of the circuit and that is connected to the neutral or grounded conductor of the system.

CIRCUIT BREAKER: A device designed to open and close a circuit by non-automatic means and to open the circuit automatically on a predetermined over current without damage to itself when properly applied within its rating.

CONCEALED: Rendered inaccessible by the structure or finish of the building. Wires in concealed raceways are considered concealed, even though they may become accessible by withdrawing them.

CONTINUOUS LOAD: A load where the maximum current is expected to continue for three hours or more.

CONTROLLER: A device or group of devices that serves to govern, in some predetermined manner, the electrical power delivered to the apparatus to which it is connected.

DEVICE: A unit of an electric system that is intended to carry or control, but not utilize, electrical energy. Units, such as switches, circuit breakers, fuse holders, receptacles, attachment plugs, and lamp holders that distribute or control but do not consume electricity are termed devices.

DISCONNECTING MEANS: A device, group of devices, or other means by which the conductors of a circuit can be disconnected from their source of supply.

DWELLING: Dwelling Unit: A single unit, providing complete and independent living facilities for one or more persons, including permanent provisions for living, sleeping, cooking and sanitation. **One Family Dwelling:** A building consisting solely of one dwelling unit. **Two Family Dwelling**: A building consisting solely of two dwelling units. Multifamily Dwelling: A building containing three or more dwelling units.

ENCLOSED: Surrounded by a case, housing, fence, or walls that prevents persons from accidentally contacting energized parts.

EQUIPMENT: A general term including material, fittings, devices, appliances, luminaries (fixtures), apparatus, and the like used as a part of, or in connection with, an electrical installation

EXPOSED: (As applied to wiring methods) On or attached to the surface or behind panels designed to allow access.

FEEDER: All circuit conductors between the service equipment or the source of separately derived system or other power supply source and the final branch-circuit overcorrect device.

GROUNDED CONDUCTOR: A system or circuit conductor that is intentionally grounded.

GROUNDING CONDUCTOR: A conductor used to connect equipment or the grounded circuit of a wiring system to a grounding electrode or electrodes.

GROUNDING CONDUCTOR, EQUIPMENT: The conductor used to connect the non-current-carrying metal parts of equipment, raceways, and other enclosures to the system grounded conductor, the grounding electrode conductor, or both at the service equipment or at the source of a separately derived system.

IDENTIFIED: (As applied to equipment) Recognizable as suitable for the specific purpose, function, use, environment, application, etc., where described in a particular Code requirement.

LOCATION: **Damp Location:** Partially protected locations under canopies, marquees, roofed open porches, and like locations, and interior locations subject to moderate degrees of moisture, such as some basements, some barns and some cold-storage warehouses. **Dry Location:** A location not normally subject to dampness or wetness. A location classified as dry may be temporarily subject to dampness or wetness, as in the case of a building under construction. **Wet Location:** Installations underground or in concrete slabs or masonry in direct contact with the earth, and locations subject to saturation with water or other liquids, such as vehicle washing areas, and locations exposed to weather and unprotected.

OUTLET: A point on the wiring system at which current is taken to supply utilization equipment.

RACEWAY: An enclosed channel designed expressly for holding wires, cables, or bus bars, with additional functions as permitted in this Code. Raceways may be of metal or nonmetallic materials. Raceways include, but are not limited to, rigid metal conduit, rigid nonmetallic conduit, intermediate metal conduit, liquid tight flexible conduit, flexible metallic tubing, flexible metal conduit, electrical nonmetallic tubing, electrical metallic tubing, under floor raceways, cellular concrete floor raceways, cellular metal floor raceways, surface raceways, wire ways, and bus ways.

RAINTIGHT: Constructed or protected so that exposure to a beating rain will not result in the entrance of water under specified test conditions.

RECEPTACLE: A receptacle is a contact device installed at the outlet for the connection of an attachment plug.

SERVICE DROP: The overhead service conductors from the last pole or other aerial support to and including the splices, if any, connecting to the service-entrance conductors at the building or other structure.

Electrical Code Terminology Pg-4

SERVICE-ENTRANCE CONDUCTORS, OVERHEAD SYSTEM: The service conductors between the terminals of the service equipment and a point usually outside the building, clear of building walls, where joined by tap or splice to the service drop.

SERVICE-ENTRANCE CONDUCTORS, UNDERGROUND SYSTEM: The service conductors between the terminals of the service equipment and the point of connection to the service lateral. Where service equipment is located outside the building walls, there may be no service entrance conductors, or they may be entirely outside the building.

SERVICE EQUIPMENT: The necessary equipment, usually consisting of a circuit breaker or switch and fuses, and their accessories, connected to the load end of service conductors to a building or other structure, or an otherwise designated area, and intended to constitute the main control and cutoff of the supply.

SPECIAL PERMISSION: The written consent of the authority having jurisdiction.

SWITCHES: **General-Use Switch:** A switch intended for use in general distribution and branch circuits. It is rated in amperes, and it is capable of interrupting its rated current at its rated voltage. **Motor-Circuit Switch:** A switch, rated in horsepower, capable of interrupting the maximum operating overload current of a motor of the same horsepower rating as the switch at the rated voltage. **Weatherproof:** Constructed or protected so that exposure to the weather will not interfere with successful operation. Rainproof, rain tight, or watertight equipment can fulfill the requirements for weatherproof where varying weather conditions other than wetness, such as snow, ice, dust, or temperature extremes, are not a factor. **Motor-Circuit Switch**: A switch, rated in horsepower, capable of interrupting the maximum operating overload current of a motor of the same horsepower rating as the switch at the rated voltage.

Always contact your local building authority for complete and up to date code information.

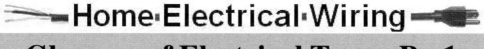
General Terms

Adapter An accessory used for interconnecting non-mating devices or converting an existing device for modified use.

Ballast A transformer that steps down AC line voltage to voltage that can be used by fluorescent or other types of lighting. Ballasts may be electromagnetic or electronic

Cord Connector A portable receptacle designed for attachment to or provided with flexible cord, not intended for fixed mounting.

Lamp holder A device with contacts that establishes mechanical and electrical connection to an inserted lamp.

Plug A device with male contacts intended for insertion into a receptacle to establish electrical connection between the attached flexible cord and the conductors connected to the receptacle.

Receptacle A device with female contacts designed for fixed installation in a structure or piece of equipment and which is intended to establish electrical connection with an inserted plug.

Switch A device for making, breaking, or changing the connections in an electric circuit.

Wallplate A plate designed to enclose an electrical box, with or without a device installed within the box.

Cord Connectors

Angle A connector that allows the attached flexible cord to exit at right angles.

Locking A connector designed to lock an inserted plug with a matching blade configuration when the plug is rotated in a clockwise direction. The plug can only be removed by first turning it in a counter-clockwise direction.

Straight Blade A non-locking connector into which mating plugs are inserted at a right angle to the plane of the connector face.

Weatherproof A connector specially constructed so that exposure to weather will not interfere with its operation.

Plugs

Angle A plug that allows the attached flexible cord to exit at right angles.

Locking A plug designed to lock into a matching connector or receptacle configuration when the plug is rotated in a clockwise direction. The plug can only be removed by turning it in a counter-clockwise direction.

Straight Blade A non-locking plug that is inserted at a right angle to the plane of the matching device face.

Weatherproof A plug specially constructed so that exposure to weather will not interfere with its operation.

Receptacles

AL/CU
30A, 50A or 60A receptacles designated for use with aluminum or copper circuit conductors, identified by "AL/CU" stamped on the device. Receptacles without this designation must never be used with aluminum circuit conductors.

Clock Hanger
A single, recessed receptacle with a specialized cover plate that provides a hook or other means of supporting a wall clock.

CO/ALR
15A or 20A receptacles designated for use with aluminum or copper circuit conductors, identified by "CO/ALR" stamped on the device. Receptacles without this designation must never be used with aluminum circuit conductors.

Duplex
Two receptacles built with a common body and mounting means; accepts two plugs.

Four-In-One or "Quad"
A receptacle in a common housing that accepts up to four plugs. Four-In-One receptacles can be installed in place of duplex receptacles mounted in a single-gang box, providing a convenient means of adding receptacles without rewiring.

GFCI (Ground Fault Circuit Interrupter)
A receptacle with a built in circuit that will detect leakage current to ground on the load side of the device. When the GFCI detects leakage current to ground, it will interrupt power to the load side of the device, preventing a hazardous ground fault condition. GFCI receptacles must conform to UL Standard 943 Class A requirements, and their use is required by the National Electric Code NFPA-70 in a variety of indoor and outdoor locations.

Interchangeable
A receptacle or combination of receptacles with a common mounting dimension that may be installed on a single or multiple-opening mounting strap.

Isolated Ground
Receptacles intended for use in an Isolated Grounding system where the ground path is isolated from the facility grounding system. The grounding connection on these receptacles is isolated from the mounting strap.

Lighted (Illuminated)
A receptacle with a face that becomes illuminated when the device is connected to an energized electrical circuit.

Locking
A receptacle designed to lock an inserted plug with a matching blade configuration when the plug is rotated in a clockwise direction. The plug can only be removed by first turning it in a counter-clockwise direction.

Safety or Tamper-Resistant
A receptacle specially constructed so that access to its energized contacts is limited. Tamper-resistant receptacles are required by the National Electric Code NFPA-70 in specific pediatric care areas in health care facilities.

Single
A receptacle that accepts only one plug.

Split-Circuit
A duplex receptacle that allows each receptacle to be wired to separate circuits. Most duplex receptacles provide break-off tabs that allow them to be converted into split-circuit receptacles.

Straight Blade
A non-locking receptacle into which mating plugs are inserted at a right angle to the plane of the receptacle face.

Glossary of Electrical Terms Pg-3

Receptacles (cont.)

Surface-Mounted	Any receptacle that mounts on a flat or plane surface.
Surge-Suppression	A receptacle with built-in circuitry designed to protect its load side from high-voltage transients and surges. The circuitry will limit transient voltage peaks to help protect sensitive electronic equipment such as PC's, modems, audio/video equipment, etc.
Triplex	A receptacle with a common mounting means which accepts three plugs.
Weatherproof	A receptacle specially constructed so that exposure to weather will not interfere with its operation.

Switches

AC/DC	A switch designated for use with either Alternating Current (AC) or Direct Current (DC).
AC Only	A switch designated for use with Alternating Current (AC) only.
Dimmer	A switch with electronic circuitry that provides DIM/BRIGHT control of lighting loads.
Door	A momentary contact switch, usually installed on a doorjamb that is activated when the door is opened or closed.
Feed-Through	An in-line switch that can be attached at any point on a length of flexible cord to provide switching control of attached equipment.
Four-Way	A switch used in conjunction with two 3-Way switches to control a single load (such as a light fixture) from three or more locations. This switch has four terminal screws and no ON/OFF marking.
Interchangeable	A switch or combination of switches with a common mounting dimension that may be installed on a single or multiple-opening mounting strap.
Low-Voltage	A switch rated for use on low-voltage circuits of 50 volts or less.
Mercury	A type of switch that uses mercury as the contact means for making and breaking an electrical circuit.
Pendant	A type of switch designed for installation at the end of a length of portable cord or cable.
Pilot Light	A switch with an integral lamp in its actuator (toggle, rocker or pushbutton) that illuminates when the switch is connected to an energized circuit and the actuator is in the ON position.
Pull	A switch where the making or breaking of contacts is controlled by pulling downward or outward on the actuator mechanism.
Push Button	A switch with an actuator mechanism that is operated by depressing a button.

Switches (cont.)

Rotary	A switch where rotating the actuator in a clockwise direction makes the circuit connection and then rotating the actuator in either the same or opposite direction breaks the connection.
Slide	A switch with a slide-action actuator for making or breaking circuit contact. Dimmer switches and fan speed controls are also available with slide-action mechanisms for lighting and fan speed control
Surface-Mounted	Any switch that mounts on a flat or plane surface.
Three-Way	A switch, always used in pairs, that controls a single load such as a light fixture from two locations. This switch has three terminal screws and has no ON/OFF marking.
Time Delay	A switch with an integral mechanism or electronic circuit that will automatically switch a load OFF at a predetermined time interval.
Timer	A switch with an integral mechanism or electronic circuit that can be set to switch an electrical load ON at a predetermined time.
Toggle	A switch with a lever-type actuator that makes or breaks switch contact as its position is changed.

Wallplates

Combination	A multiple- gang wallplate with openings in each gang to accommodate different devices.
Deco	Wallplates with Decorative size openings available in a variety of multiple-gang configurations.
Flush	A wallplate designed for flush-mounting with wall surfaces or the plane surfaces of electrical equipment.
Gang	A term that describes the number of devices a wallplate is sized to fit (i.e. "2- gang" designates two devices).
Oversized	Wallplates that are approx. 3/4" higher and wider than the standard size and are used to conceal greater wall irregularities than those hidden by Midway wallplates. These wallplates are approx. 1/4" deep to ensure a proper fit when used with protruding devices.
Modular	Individual-section wallplates with different openings that can be configured into a multi-gang plate.
Multi-Gang	A wallplate that has two or more gangs.
Tandem	A wallplate with individual gangs arranged vertically one above the other.
Weatherproof (with Cover Closed)	A UL Listed cover that meets specific test standards for use in wet and damp locations with the cover closed.
Weatherproof (with Cover Open)	A UL Listed cover that meets specific test standards for use in wet and damp locations with the cover open or closed.

BONUS Section

BONUS SECTION

Home·Electrical·Wiring

How to Select an Electrical Contractor Pg-1

10 Tips to Make Sure Your Electrical Contractor Measures Up

 1. Hire only state licensed contractors.

If your "electrician" or "contractor" is not licensed and something should go wrong with your project you may have very little recourse. Professional electrical contractors are licensed by the state licensing bureau or governing agency. If something goes wrong on your project then you may choose to file a complaint. Complaints are typically verified and inspected and if found to be valid can result in fines, suspensions or loss of license to the offending contractor. If your "electrician" or "contractor" does not have a license, then he or she has nothing to lose.

 2. Check a contractor's license number online or by phone.

A contractor's license may be verified by contacting the local state contractors licensing department either by phone or using the internet. This gives you the ability to make see if the license is up to date or not. You may also be able to see if there have been any complaints filed against the contractor.

 3. Get at least three bids.

Three bids will be very helpful to compare the contractors and proposed work. If you see a large difference between the bids you may ask questions about the reason why and inquire about the type of materials that will be installed. Make sure the bid is itemized and pay close attention to items such as light fixture types and styles to make sure you are getting the quality that you desire. An itemized bid will help you understand what the contractor plans to do. This will avoid the possibility of "underestimating" the job in order to get the contract which can result in unexpected expenses.

 4. Get three references from each bidder and review past work in person.

Obtaining references is vital, especially if they compare to the same type of work you need to have done. If the company cannot produce these references then you may have a cause to be suspicious.

 5. Make sure all project expectations are in writing and only sign the contract if you completely understand the terms.

A full set of plans describing the project with specific information may be required in order to bid the project accurately. The plan should include information relating to specific equipment that may require a dedicated power circuit for special equipment. Review the itemized list of materials where less expensive but comparable or equivalent materials may be used to reduce the cost of the project. Be aware that sometimes such items are used to increase the contractor's profit. Make sure that you are getting what you are paying for and that you are not paying any more than you have to. Be sure that you are aware of all of the options such as the style and color of receptacles and switches. Do you desire regular or the stylish type, such as Decora, and do you want the light fixtures to be controlled by a dimmer switch, if so what kind of dimmer controls would you like? Contractors have options that may allow you to get more for your money just by asking the right questions.

How to Select an Electrical Contractor Pg-2

10 Tips to Make Sure Your Electrical Contractor Measures Up (cont.)

 6. Confirm that the contractor has workers' compensation insurance for employees.
Most state laws require workers to be covered with compensation insurance, however the sole owner of a business or a one man shop may not required to have workers compensation insurance. If your area requires the company to carry workers' compensation insurance for their employees then they must prove that they do, otherwise they are violating the law. Keep in mind that if a worker gets hurt on your job and there is no workers' compensation insurance in place then you may be held liable. In most areas contractors should have a minimum $1,000,000 general liability policy. If they do not and something should go wrong then you may be held liable.

 7. Never pay more than 10% down or $1,000, whichever is less.
Don't pay in cash.
Along with the itemized quote or bid proposal the selling price should be clearly displayed showing that 10% will be required at the acceptance or signing of the contract. In most cases the project will not begin until this payment has been received. Pay close attention to the language used in the proposal contract for a full understanding.

 8. Don't let payments get ahead of the work.
The proposal contract should show any scheduled progressive payments that will become due and payable during certain phases of the project. For example 30% may be due when the rough or first inspection has taken place and the inspection has passed. Any changes such as the deletion or the addition of circuits or devices should be written up in a Change Order which documents the change specifically, including the cost or credit for parts and materials and the associated labor. In most cases, if the change order is an addition to the project a payment may be required, and any additional time may need to be factored into the timeline of the entire project.

 9. Keep a job file of all papers relating to your project, including all payments.
Be sure that the time schedule is as specific as possible whether your project is large or small. Ask the contractor what they plan to do when and when they plan to finish each phase of the project. Make sure that you understand the description of what will be done, and that the timeline relates to the time estimate that was given to you.

 10. Don't make the final payment until you're satisfied with the job.
The project must have passed the final inspection and all necessary components that were not covered by the inspection, such as low voltage devices should be installed before the final payment has been made. If there has been a delay in receiving special finish or trim parts then allow for these expenses and discuss them with the contractor.

This is an example of the guidelines you may want to adopt when selecting an electrical contractor to do work for you. Contact your state or area for their specific guidelines.

Purchasing from a Wholesale Supplier Pg-1

Let's get Serious about the Electrical Parts you Need

Be sure to ask about the supplier's prices. Typically a wholesale house does not have price tags, unlike Home Depot and Lowe's where you know what you're going to pay before you check out. The pricing at most wholesale suppliers is going to be best for the most common materials and is based on corporate purchasing agreements which are influenced by market prices.

Venturing Into "The Contractor Zone"
Let's get Serious about the Electrical Parts you Need
I would advise you to get a few comparative prices for the non-common types of materials. Material costs add up fast and it may be worthwhile to either talk to your supplier about discount prices for your project or make phone calls and compare prices and brands.

My Personal Perspective on Electrical Wholesale Supply Companies
In tough economic times we all need to be careful with our resources, however to choose correctly for not only yourself but the people you do business with is important to me. From a contractor's perspective it is difficult doing business with any material supplier who does not make good use of the technology tools that are available, not only at the local supply house but on the corporate side as well. Now I will admit that I am a little more techno-savvy then your average contractor, but I sincerely feel that those who choose not to learn about and use today's technology will suffer in the duration, and the same goes for corporate wholesale suppliers. I have witnessed firsthand large companies who choose not to advance with technology, and some who make wrong decisions because of a lack of understanding, and this is a disservice not only to themselves but to their clients as well. The bottom line is to do business with those who offer good value and great service.

Having a well throughout system that enables account holders to access their account online to the point of seamlessly accessing their past purchasing transactions and downloading this information into their Contractor Billing Software is just one example. Being able to place orders online is another, and this is all possible, the technology is already in place and ready to implement.

So what's the problem? I would answer money and the right people. Decisions are being made through out the industry that will either make or break the future of any company. The business for a particular industry such as electrical will always be in demand, but those who make the right choices will be the leaders.

Locating a Good Electrical Supply House
Wholesale supply houses can be found in your area, and many will allow DIY'ers to purchase from them. If you are planning a major remodel project you may want to apply for an account and possibly receive a discount on your materials.

Purchasing from a Wholesale Supplier Pg-2

A Visit to the Local Supply House
Unlike the typical Home Depot or Lowe's, your local electrical wholesale supply house is generally a non-formal place to visit because it is geared for selling mainly to licensed contractors who gather at a counter and tell the counter salesman what they need.

Electrical Materials
I have seen folks come into a supply house and ask about how to do certain projects. You must understand that many people who work at a supply house have limited experience with the trade and may not be able to help you. Their specialty is knowing about their parts and selling them to you. Some on the other hand may have an experienced person working there, or possibly a friendly contractor at the counter who may be willing to help you out.

Free Electrical Advice
Let me mention that you could experience a mixed atmosphere while at the supply house - especially if it is filled with a lot of contractors. The supplier has to be careful about giving homeowners "Free Advice" – let's face it, they have no idea what your abilities are or how you are going to interpret the information they may share with you - not to mention liability.

Home Electrical Projects - Your Decision - Your Liability
Understand that as a do-it-yourselfer, you assume ALL Responsibility for Your Work - It is YOUR DECISION to take on your project and you choose to accept Full Responsibility for what You Do. Asking questions about how to do something can put a supplier and contractor in an uncomfortable position. I've heard this happen many times. I have spoken with homeowners to try to help them, but if I ever sense that they are unqualified, I always encourage them to hire a qualified professional to do their work.

Electricians and the Economy
Another situation you may "feel" is that you may be standing amongst contractors who are in need of work, and there standing along side of them at the counter is a homeowner who is doing a project themselves - in essence, doing a job the contractor would love to be hired to do. So just be aware of these conditions that you could experience. Just remember, we contractors want to feed our families too!

Purchasing from a Wholesale Supplier Pg-3

Extensive Electrical Parts and Tools
One thing for sure is that your local electrical wholesale suppliers will have access to virtually any electrical part you may need, and most of the time it is on the shelf, and if not they can have it for you within a matter of days.

Most Electrical Wholesale Suppliers are Open to the Public
I've encountered two scenarios with the wholesale supply house and homeowners. One is that the supplier accepts them; the other is that they are closed to them and they do business only with licensed contractors. The latter is not the case in most areas because the supply house wants your business. Part of this is due to so many contractors doing business with the large competitors such as Home Depot and Lowe's, however most supply houses really want to support the homeowner, in fact - several have added displays and showrooms to help you see some of their product lines. A wholesale supplier does not have aisles for you to push a cart down, but rather a counter where you tell the sales person what you need, then they go gather your parts.

Make the Calls - Ask the Questions
Here's what I recommend: First - understand what parts you need for your project. This publication will do its best to provide project information with a material lists. Second - locate your local supply house(s), and give them a call. Ask for either a Manager or the Accounts Representative. Tell them who you are and give them the basics of what you're doing, but don't go into a big explanation - keep in mind, most supply houses are dealing with busy contractors who are waiting to get their parts so they can get back out to their jobs. Be specific about your parts list, ask them if they carry the parts you're looking for; then listen to their response. This will give you an indication of whether you want to do business with them or not. Keep in mind - they are an "Electrical Supply House" not an "Electrical Information Center".

The Homeowner Do-It-Yourselfer Market
I should point something out here - there are a lot of "Do-It-Yourself" books which may not be written by Electrical Contractors. The majority of the pictures that you see in those books are of hired "models" not contractors. You can tell by looking at their tools - they are always brand new, and they never make a mess- Amazing! Well folks, these books are written with the DIY'er in mind, and they know that the majority of these people will go to one of the big hardware stores to buy their parts. There are many of these types of parts you will never find at a contractor's wholesale supply house. Why?, because the pros use the materials the pros use, and the DIY'er hardware stores are locked into purchasing channels that are geared towards high profit margins. Oh sure - these parts will get the job done just fine, but understand that they may not be the same grade of material or quality that a professional electrical contractor would install.

How to Purchase Materials for the Best Price

Good Deals for Tools and Parts

The Internet
Big Box Hardware Stores
Wholesale Suppliers
Today we have more options for purchasing then ever before, and by spending a little time you could save a lot of money and get a great deal, especially on tools and light fixtures which are not found at most local wholesale supply houses.
Note: If you buy over the internet make sure the parts are authentic brand names and UL Approved.

Surf a Little and Save a Lot

The Internet - Thank Goodness for Shopping Searches and Amazon

If you know what you're looking for you will find several places to buy on the internet. It would be best to have the make and model or part number to make sure your researching the right item.
Amazon, eBay, Bing, Yahoo and Google Shopping Searches will all reveal the best price, but look out for shipping charges which could easily double the price. The good thing is that you can get a good idea about the range of competitive pricing.

Big Box Stores - Home Depot and Lowe's

These big box stores have the best deal on items that sell fast and in bulk. These are usually the items they put in their fliers to get you into the store. I have found great deals on Type-NM wire, bulk packs of rough-in boxes, plugs, switches and covers, circuit breakers and panels, lamps, bulbs and light fixtures.

Your Local Wholesale Supplier - Support Your Community

I like to support my local wholesale suppliers as much as possible, and besides they are a bunch of great guys and gals that work there and they live in my area. Most of the times I know these guys are giving me a great price, and I even ask them, but it is really helpful to have my research pricing info on hand so I can see how the total price will be. It takes me time and gas money to drive to a big box store, so if my wholesaler can treat me fairly then I'm happy to give them my business.

Home·Electrical·Wiring

Indexes

Index of Circuit Design Tables

Index of Electrical Codes Pg-1

Index of Electrical Codes Pg-3

Index of Code Tables

Home·Electrical·Wiring

Index of Materials Pg-2

Home·Electrical·Wiring

Index of Wiring Diagrams Pg-1

Home·Electrical·Wiring

Index of Wiring Diagrams Pg-2

Index of Wiring Plans

Main Index

Conclusion

I hope this book has helped you with your home electrical wiring projects.

I will be developing more resources which will be available soon so please check back to see our list of new publications.

Visit me at:
www.Ask-The-Electrician.com
or the book website at:
www.Home-Electrical-Wiring.com

Dave

I love to hear from my readers, so let me know how this book has helped you and what other electrical topics you would like to learn about.

Do you want more Home Electrical Tips?

By subscribing to my free newsletter, you will receive valuable electrical wiring tips, featured questions, special offers and much more!

Also available from: www.Ask-The-Electrician.com

The 10 Mistakes and How to Avoid Them

How to Wire 3-Way Switches

Outdoor Lighting

Solar Landscape Lighting

Home·Electrical·Wiring

Reviews and Testimonials

Dave - This is really a great book!
Very helpful for the homeowner.
Kathleen Koolstra

Hello David,
This book is very detailed and full of information.
Patrick H. Schwartz

Wow! Dave, the book is awesome, I really Like It.
It looks very professional, I think it's going to be a great help for homeowners.
Congratulations!
Ken Meffan

Hi Dave
You must feel a great sense of accomplishment
and relief to finally get your book written.
Randy Whitlock

Resources

RESOURCES

Resources - Organizations

 **This is a brief listing of some electrical organizations and trade media.**

Organizations

- **Habitat for Humanity** - Great for Learning and Helping Others
  www.habitat.org/cd/local/

- **IEC** - Independent Electrical Contractors
  www.ieci.org

- **IEEE** - Institute of Electrical and Electronics Engineers
  www.ieee.org

- **NECA** -National Electrical Contractors Association
  www.necaconnection.org

- **NACHI** - National Association of Certified Home Inspectors
  www.nachi.org

- **NFPA** - National Fire Protection Association
  www.nfpa.org
- **UL** - Underwriters Laboratories
  www.ul.com

Media

- **Electrical Construction & Maintenance**
  www.ecmweb.com

- **Electrical Contractor**
  www.ecmag.com

Resources - Wholesalers & Manufacturers

 This is a brief listing of some electrical wholesalers and manufacturers.

Wholesalers

- CED - Consolidated Electrical Distributors
- Graybar
- Grainger
- Rexel
- WESCO - Westinghouse Supply

Manufacturers

- Parts
  - Arlington
  - Garvin
  - Grainger
  - Hubbell
  - Leviton
  - Lutron
  - Schneider
  - Siemens
  - Thomas & Betts

- Tools
  - Bosh
  - DeWalt
  - Klein
  - Milwaukee
  - Ryobi

- Testers
  - Greenlee
  - Fluke
  - Siemens

Credits and Acknowledgements

 Resources Listed in this Publication

Resource

- **Clients, Contractors and Job sites**
  - CCI
  - Heidi Agler, Architect
  - Ken Meffan, Architect
  - Thompson Construction
  - Vanson Construction

- **Agencies and Utilities**
  - CSLB
  - PG&E
  - SPP
  - El Dorado County
  - Nevada County
  - Placer County

- **Local Wholesale Suppliers**
  - CED
  - Rexel

- **Special Lighting Fixtures**
  - Alpha Omega Wagon Wheel Furniture

Copyrights and Trademarks belong to the appropriate companies including:

- NEC National Electrical Code, NFPA National Fire Prevention Assoc.
- Romex - Southwire Corp.
- Jenn Air - Jenn Air Corp. UL Underwriters Laboratory
- General Electric Company

Printed in Great Britain
by Amazon